NAVIGATING
LIFE
book 1

Resources, Direction & Answers for Anxiety,
Depression, PTSD, Sexual Abuse,
Personality Disorders, Grief and more...

NAVIGATING
LIFE

When and How to Involve a Professional

CRAIG T. MITCHELL, LCSW

NAVIGATING LIFE: Resources:Direction & Answers for Anxiety, Depression, PTSD, Sexual Abuse, Personality Disorders, Grief and More...
by Craig T. Mitchell, LCSW
©2019 Craig T. Mitchell, LCSW

Edited by Mylynn Felt, Joan Williams and Natalia Burdett
Cover design by Dan Pitts of Dan Pitts Design
danpitts.com
Interior book design by Russell Elkins of Inky's Nest Design

ISBN: 978-1-950741-00-7

Published by Inky's Nest Publishing

1st edition
First printed in 2019 in the United States of America

CONTENTS

Introduction **9**

1 My Background and Reasons for Writing This Book **13**

2 The Healing Process **27**

3 Anxiety Definition and Treatment **39**

4 Depression Definition and Treatment **51**

5 Postpartum Depression **63**

6 Grief **69**

7 Posttraumatic Stress Disorder **79**

8 Victims of Sexual Abuse **83**

9 Personality Disorders: Living and Dealing with Very Difficult People **111**

10 Psychosis, Schizophrenia and Bipolar Disorder **147**

11 Psychiatrists, Psychologists, Psychotherapists, Social Workers, What Is the Difference? **153**

12 Medication for Mental Health Treatment **161**

13 Counseling or Psychotherapy: What Is It and Who Does It? **169**

14 How to Find a Therapist or Counselor **179**

Acknowledgments

I would like to thank many individuals who have been instrumental in shaping the direction I have taken in this life. First, I would like to thank my family. My parents provided an example of hard work. They were always there to back me up when I needed support, and they also provided no small amount of help in the form of more hard work on my behalf. My wife, Arlette, was instrumental in teaching me about loving everyone, especially those with special needs. She was truly a Saint who advocated for and took these individuals into our home to give their families needed rest from around the clock care. She was loved by those she cared for and their families. She was also a great mother and disciplined our seven children with tough love when it was needed. My children grew up loving each other and were very patient to accept the other children who came into our home on a regular basis. I am so proud of the contributions they are all making to this world.

One of my high school teachers, James Dorigatti, was instrumental in leading me into my profession as a therapist. The most prominent teachers in my life are Dr. Gary Carson, a psychology professor from college, and JoAnn Larson from graduate school. I can't put in words the inspiration these two people have been to me. I have tried, unsuccessfully, to emulate their professionalism and want them to know how much they influenced my career choices.

I want to thank my patients who over the years have been the reason I love to do therapy. I have always tried to be the best therapist I could for them. I know for some I was not a good fit, just as all doctors or products are not the best for everyone. In these cases, I tried to send them to others who might be better for them. I have learned everything from them and thank them for trusting me to help them get to a better place in life.

I thank my friends who have been there for me, from high school to today. I thank Mylynn Felt, my first editor, Joanie Williams for her input and editing, and Natalia Burdett who was my final editor. I also thank Stephanie Stockdale for her encouragement and prodding during the past several years. I need pushing and she provided it. I am grateful for Russell Elkins and Dan Pitts for their professional guidance and professionalism. I thank Matt Anderson for his work on the illustrations. Most of all I am grateful for the constant prompting from the creator of us all and the blessings of having such a variety of professional and life experiences, which I believe prepared me to write these books.

INTRODUCTION

Getting Help for You and Your Family

I wrote this book because I want to help families and individuals get the help they need for many of the problems they might experience in life. I hope someday to expand and add another volume to give families even more direction for other challenges facing them. Most of what is included in this work reflects my own professional and personal experiences throughout the years.

Do you have a child, maybe yourself or someone in your life with some kind of problem or a basic need and you don't know where to turn for help? You may have read articles or books and asked questions of parents, family members, school teachers, the family doctor or even mental health professionals. You might be worried that you're not providing your child with the necessary parenting or treatment to help him or her overcome delays or behaviors that are unacceptable or just not what you think is, "normal." Are you struggling with issues of your own and don't know where to turn? Maybe you know what you should do, but you are afraid to take the steps necessary to receive help or make a change. If this is the case, and it is for many families, then you are the person I hope this book speaks to.

If you are dealing with a problem it can be confusing and you may be filled with doubts about which direction you should take, especially if you are a young parent, and you have a sixth sense or a feeling that something is not right with your child. You may have said to yourself. "I think my child or someone I care about needs help, and I can't stop worrying. What do I do, and where do I go for answers?"

I do not want to give anyone the impression that this book is your answer regarding any subject. I am simply providing information, and if you find that it describes or touches on something you might need to know, then my purpose for writing the book will, in part, be achieved. I always recommend that you contact your health care provider (which for many people is their family doctor) for advice. Nothing anyone writes will ever supersede a visit with a caring, concerned doctor, therapist, trained professional or whoever you trust for the care of you or your family. You should always seek local professional help when you have a concern. In some cases, people go for years and suffer needlessly because they don't know where to turn or don't know help is available. This is something I want to change for those of you who read this book. I hope to make you aware of a number of conditions, circumstances and problems that I have had exposure to during my years of working with people in a variety of settings.

The majority of information in this book reflects experiences I have had in each area. I will draw on other professionals and organizations for information as well as real life examples which I think everyone should be aware. I will introduce you to these experts and I hope you will purchase their books and research them to become more educated in their areas of expertise. My desire is to expose you to the work of many competent professionals who can provide even more information and knowledge you may need.

One Book Became Three

When I began writing this book I intended it to be one book, however as I kept addressing all the areas I wanted to discuss I wound up with almost 50 chapters. Additionally, I have many more chapters I want to educate the public on, if this effort is successful. I was told that no one would read one book with that many chapters, but they would read smaller books with fewer, related subjects. Due to separating the chapters into three more manageable books, one book may refer to a section of one of the other two books. I do this not because I want you to purchase more books, but because so many concepts throughout the book apply to many different areas of our lives. You may not read all three books because you may not have interest in all of the subject matter. I believe that most people will be touched by or know of people who have experienced most of the conditions described in these books before they leave this life. I will also mention some concepts and refer you to other chapters within the books for ideas or other programs of which you should have specific knowledge.

Changing the Minds of People Today About Mental Health, Counseling or Therapy

I had two major goals in writing this book. The first is my desire to change the way people think about seeking counseling and to encourage people to get help for mental-emotional problems. Secondly, I want families and individuals to find more help, if it exists out there, for those who have special needs. Mingled within both of these subjects lie many other issues to understand and be aware of. I also want to encourage action and initiative within those who either need or seek help because they may need to create, from the ground up, the resource they are searching for which they are searching. This is because there are far too few resources out there for the multitude of mental-emotional needs we have as people. I do not want to give those who read this book the impression that I will show them the answers to all their problems, because depending on where a person lives there may be literally nowhere to turn to find a resource for his or her concerns. Some ideas in this book may be helpful in finding answers, but you may need to be the answer for yourself and possibly many others by starting a support group or organization that will make a difference for those who need what you can offer.

Concepts You Need to Know

In over 39 years of practice I have come across a number of ideas and concepts I use in therapy that I think you should understand. I have included many of these ideas throughout this book as I explain how I conduct therapy. I want you to understand what other authors have said that I think are critical to make better sense of life. I hope as you read you will apply these important concepts to yourself, your family and that you will be open to acquiring books from other authors I refer to. Simply put, I have found excellent ideas from other professionals, and we can all benefit from some of the best minds who have made life better for all of us.

One last word before we start. I have given the name of many authors, books, articles, websites and much more information, but that does not mean that there are not many other excellent ideas and resources for each area I cover. There simply was not enough room in this work to cite all the great and helpful information that exists. My advice to you is, when you read a subject you have interest in, do some more research. There is a plethora of information out there to be found.

chapter one
BACKGROUND AND MOTIVATION FOR THIS BOOK

My Background

As I begin this book I believe you need to know my background so you understand where I get my thoughts and experience. I was born in a small town and because of better employment opportunities my family moved to a city. My father was a painter and a very hard working man who could roll paint on a wall in his 80's faster than anyone I have ever seen. He had a motto which you have all heard at one time or other, "If you are going to do something, do it right." We were not well-off financially, but between my mother who worked at a wedding reception center and my dad's employment we did not lack for anything. I remember my mother saying to me when I started my first job as a dishwasher at the reception center, "You are going to have to buy your own clothes now because you have a job." When I heard this, I was proud as I could be because she gave me the responsibility to take care of my own needs, and I felt I had been given a badge of trust. I was just 14 at the time and I felt empowered and grown up, and I will never forget that feeling of confidence she placed in me.

As a teenager I was exposed to a teacher who taught me about positive mental attitude and a few years later I had another great teacher in my life who took this concept to a higher level. I believe we can accomplish anything we desire and I have seen great things happen to ordinary people who take their dreams and make them into reality.

My Motivation for Writing This Book

Twenty-five years ago, I was reading a book and, all of a sudden, I had the strangest feeling that I was supposed to write a book, sometime in my life. That was a surreal experience, feeling such a prompting, but I knew it would happen and that it was one of my purposes in this life. I can't explain it, but this feeling has never left me. A little over seven years ago I began having very strong impressions that I needed to start this work, so I began. As I put my mind to the task, I had an awakening of sorts because I realized that my life's work as a Social Worker has taken me through a rich smorgasbord of experiences that have blessed my life. Without these experiences, I could not have written this book.

My Professional and Life Experiences: The Basis for This Book

Right out of high school my friend called me one morning and told me he was going to barber school so he could work his way through college with a trade. Sitting there in my boxer shorts I said, "Sounds good; I think I'll go with you." I hung up the phone and told my mother, "I'm going to barber school," and then went back to bed. So I spent nine months in barber school, worked three months as a barber and then did some volunteer work in Oregon, Idaho, California, and Washington for a couple of years. This was my first exposure to understanding people, and what an invaluable education it was! From the time I returned home and started my college education I worked as a barber. The reason I bring this up is because a barber shop is another great place to get an education. I attended college and received a Bachelor's Degree in Psychology. During this time I had a practicum at an agency where I had a chance to get some exposure to counseling. This was another great experience since I was able to participate in training from a brilliant psychiatrist. At one time he had a patient named Kim Peek, who was the inspiration for the movie Rain Man.

When I entered graduate school in Social Work I felt like I was betraying the field of Psychology because in those days, Social Work was the poor little brother to Psychology. I did so because I wanted to work for a particular agency who was hiring Master's Degree level, Social Workers. While attending graduate school, I worked a graveyard shift at an urban Job Corp Center. An urban center meant that we had kids there who were from large metropolitan cities. Back then a sizable number of our student population were youth who were in trouble with the law. The court system gave them the option of probation/jail or Job Corp. Can you guess which option they chose? We had some pretty tough characters there. Thank goodness for a few staff members who taught me how to survive in that place. During this first year of graduate school, I had a practicum at a facility where all of the juvenile delinquents in the state were incarcerated. I was there two full 8-hour days per week working with the "students," as they were referred to. The professor who was our supervisor in that setting was a remarkable woman named JoAnn Larsen. Each week every graduate student she supervised met with her and had to produce two, one-page, single-spaced, typed documents, detailing the comments and responses between the graduate students and two of the juveniles he or she counseled with that week. That was intimidating and a meat grinder, but I learned how to do therapy. It is because of her that I left graduate school with the confidence that I could help people in therapy. She is my inspiration along with another professor of psychology in my undergraduate education named Gary Carson. In my second year of graduate school I was asked by Dr. Larsen if I wanted to work with her to complete a publishable paper instead of doing a thesis, and I jumped at the chance. I worked with the juveniles at the same facility previously mentioned and compiled all the data which she used to write an article entitled, "Strength Oriented, Task Centered, Group Work with Delinquents," which was published in Social Case Work.

In my second year of graduate school my practicum was at the agency where I would eventually be hired after graduation. This was the same agency that provided my practical experience with in college. I was hired on as a full-time, graveyard supervisor with the

Youth Development Center where I had spent time in my previous year's practicum. Dealing with those juvenile delinquents was a breeze compared to the individuals at Job Corp. I appreciate the lessons learned from all these facilities because they are lessons I will never forget. During my two years in graduate school, I would go to work by 11:00 p.m. and work until 7:00 a.m. then go to my in-laws, sleep for a few hours, get up, and (depending on the day of the week) go to my practicum or to school 35 miles away and then go to the barber shop for a few hours, head home and be with my wife and two children at the time, study then sleep a bit and start the process over again. Good thing I did this when I was young.

I was hired on to the agency I wanted to work for right out of graduate school and moved to Washington State. When I arrived at work the first day, I had a full schedule of clinical appointments. I was green out of school and walked into the first appointment of my fledgling career with a couple who was there for marriage counseling. The husband said, "If you can't help us then we are getting a divorce." No pressure! Not only was I booked up with therapy appointments, but I was also given the responsibility for what was called Licensed Services, which included a Foster Care Program, a Birth Parent Program and an Adoptive Parent Program. I was given the manuals for these three programs, with no training mind you, and told if I had any questions to just ask. Each binder was an inch and a half thick. When I finally got through all three manuals I didn't know the difference between a birth parent, foster child, or adoptive parent. This was overwhelming along with my full load of clinical appointments. However, I learned very quickly because I was in the frying pan, literally. It took a while to learn the details of my responsibilities with some help from a good friend who eventually came to my location to manage the office. I became attached to the people I worked with, the kids in foster care and their families as well as the adoption program, especially the birth mothers and adoptive parents. I found myself going with birth mothers to court and asking them questions on the witness stand to relinquish their parental rights. I saw and felt of their grief, strength, and determination to do for their child what they felt was best. These were selfless individuals who became heroes in my eyes. I picked up babies from hospitals all over Eastern Washington and Northern Idaho and saw the joy in the faces of the families who were blessed by these little lives. I was witness to what many people would call coincidence as we received input from birth parents and matched the babies with the adoptive couples. I saw a number of what I call miracles and I grew to love those brave young women of exceptional character, no matter what their choice was.

I traveled to several small towns to work with birth parents, adoptive parents and families who had children in foster care as well as the foster parents. I also taught a parenting course in all these areas and trained people to teach this course in their communities. I did a lot of therapy in these places with individuals, couples, and families. I came to understand that in these outlying areas longer therapy sessions worked much better because when I was only there once or twice a month the process needed to be accelerated and meeting for 90 minutes to two hours really made a difference. I started applying the same session length at my own office and found it to be just as effective, and I preferred it with many of my clients rather than the 50 minute sessions, which is what most therapists do. Wrapping up an important concept in a longer session can be vital to the progress of the client. You can imagine how it goes over when I have to say, "Oh time is up, let's schedule another appointment so we can finish what we are doing here today."

I began giving a personality test I used in my graduate work at the agency where I was trained. I came to know the MMPI or Minnesota Multiphasic Personality Inventory well because I gave it to almost all of my clients for a dozen years. This is important because this test can be the door to the soul for those who take it. It is so completely revealing about a person's personality that it can help identify what a person needs to work on in therapy or if a family member is struggling, it is precise in identifying what is really going on. It can help you decide if the person you are considering committing to in marriage is free from troubling problems. This is not 100% guaranteed, but it is without question, the most accurate way I know of to learn what the true personality of anyone really is. I will address this test in Book 3 in the chapter on CONSIDERING MARRIAGE.

During my first year of practice, I discovered that approximately 50% of the women I saw in therapy had been sexually abused in some way or other. When I realized this, I began asking everyone I saw if this had ever happened to them. I became an advocate for victims of sexual abuse. Working with Adults Molested as Children, (AMAC) as they are called, is the most gratifying work I do. I feel as I am working with them that I am walking on sacred ground. I not only did individual therapy with them, but I also ran many AMAC groups. This continues to be one of my crusades in life, to help these people recover, gain self-love and to learn how to live life without guilt, shame, and the shackles that accompany these victims.

Most of my work in therapy during the 80s and 90s was with individuals experiencing depression. That has changed over the years, and now anxiety is the most common condition I see. I have done marriage counseling during these years and have witnessed all kinds of situations in marriage. I used to think that any marriage can be salvaged, but I am a bit wiser now. Personality disorders is one of the main reasons marriages do not survive, which I address in this book, and I believe it is something that is vital for everyone to understand. Do not skip that chapter! I have seen all kinds of mental health diagnoses, and I have struggled in my own marriage and found ways to make it work and thrive. I believe most marriages will have challenges because that is what I have observed, and it is a part of life.

I have seven children, so I understand what challenges parenting presents. After teaching the parenting class I referred to in Eastern Washington and Northern Idaho for over 10 years, I saw how learning new skills as a parent can make a remarkable difference not only for children but the parents as well.

My Family's Experience with Special Needs

My wife had a desire to work with special needs children, and she first got that opportunity with a colleague of mine who had a son with cerebral palsy. This is when I was introduced to what is called Respite Care. This is a program where parents who have children with special needs can receive a break from the care of their child for a few hours, a day here or there, or up to a weekend or longer depending on how they use their allotted hours. In order to do this, we had to be licensed as foster parents. It wasn't long before my wife had about 12 kids she was taking care of. Not all at once of course, but there were times I would come home from work, and there would be two or three kids there for a few hours until their parents picked them up later that day. I recall coming home one day, walking in the family room and seeing three special needs kids, two of which I had never seen before. At first I thought I was in the wrong house, but I knew my wife had said yes to more parents in need. She was incredible and seemed to know exactly what to do with these kids. She cared for some who were completely incapacitated and non-ambulatory, others who needed to be fed with feeding tubes, some had tracheotomies with breathing tubes in their throats. We had all kinds of these special children in and out of our home on a regular basis. Some of them would need to be watched carefully because they would get into food or other things, and some would take off running and would have to be chased down. My own kids became experts at understanding, accepting and, at times, chasing and helping retrieve these kids. My children are amazing, and they advocate for special needs people; I am extremely proud of each of them. At one point in time we had a foster daughter who lived with us for three years, and for the first six months or so she would spend a weekend on occasion when her parents would take her. They hadn't received any services over the years and by the time their daughter was 13 when we took her, they were very much in need of a break from her 24-hour care. Let me assure you that they loved her completely and her mother was heavily ridden with guilt as she let her come to our home, but they needed the respite care desperately. This young girl had cerebral palsy, epilepsy, blindness, and had no speech. Her poor body tone was so stiff that it was difficult to get her from her bed to the bath tub and into a wheelchair or vehicle. When her parents started taking her every weekend it was a great blessing for us. Feeding her was 45 minutes of struggle because of her gag reflex and trouble swallowing. This is common with those who have cerebral palsy. Over time, she had a feeding tube placed in her stomach which allowed feeding with what is called a bolus or a large syringe which is connected to a tube in her stomach. Formula or puréed food is prepared and drained into the stomach using gravity. An automatic pump is also used, most often at night to provide nutrition efficiently. Medications were constantly being administered to her to control her seizures and keep her hyper tone level (stiffness) down, as well as other necessary medications. Eventually, her parents were able to receive some in-home services, and when this happened they took her back into their home. If they would have had such services before, she would not have come to live with us. They would only have required some respite care for weekends or at other times instead of longer term care in or home. This is another reason I wrote this book, to make people aware of the imperative need for more in-home and respite services to allow children to remain in their homes instead of placing them in more expensive institutional situations or foster care. The difference in the cost between these programs is tremendous as respite care is much less costly and more desirable.

As time passed we had some older special needs individuals who came to our home, and they are very special people. I learned much from them and their grateful parents and families who had the chance to recharge their batteries, so to speak, as they were able to go on dates and vacations and other activities they were unable to before receiving respite services. We need more respite services for these amazing families who carry such heavy burdens.

Pioneer Living

I believe I should include a couple of experiences my family has gone through, and that is the fact that we built two homes from the ground up. I was the general contractor and had to identify and hire subcontractors to complete specific construction requirements. I had to oversee all the work and contact the county inspectors to schedule the required inspections for footings, foundation, rough plumbing, electrical, mechanical (heat and cooling), framing, and all the finish work. I had the footings, foundation, rough plumbing, framing and half the sheetrock contracted out. The rest I did with the help of my wife and some very good friends and family. There were times when several church members would come to help, and it reminded me of the old days when neighbors would come over for a barn raising. It took us about a year to get in both homes, and I am grateful for the help we received. I spent a lot of late nights working on two different homes, but it was well worth it.

When we moved into the first home we built, the only room that was finished was the laundry room. Our three older children slept on mattresses in that room, on the floor. The only bathroom completed was on the second floor, and for the first week or two we had to use a trouble light when it was dark. There were no kitchen cabinets, no carpet except for the laundry room, and my wife and I slept on a bed in the family room, which was on a cement slab. We cooked on a hot plate and microwave on a picnic table, which was in the pantry. We washed dishes in a laundry tub in the laundry room. There were six bedrooms on the second floor and only two were sheet rocked when we moved in. It took us several more months to finish all the work and, in the meantime, it was very much "pioneer living." The funny thing is that my wife and I never got along better nor had so much fun as when we were finishing our homes. She was a tough woman and worked right alongside me when she wasn't seeing to the needs of the little ones. I don't want to think of what kind of father I was during these times.

More Diverse Employment Opportunities

After living in Washington State for 13 years, we moved back to Utah where I had a job with an insurance company to authorize mental health benefits for employees of large companies. These were usually stays in treatment programs for drug and alcohol or psychiatric hospitals. This gave me a different view of what insurance companies are really like. Many people see insurance companies as evil and as agencies that won't pay for treatments. However, I learned very quickly that the companies who purchase insurance coverage for their employees dictate exactly what they will and won't pay for prior to buying the package they purchase. What the insurance company covers is spelled out in detail when coverage begins. There were times when some kind of need was not covered by the insurance package a business had purchased and we would recommend the employee call the human resource office of the company they worked for and ask if they would pay for the coverage since it was not covered in their plan. Sometimes these companies would do so and really come through for their employees. The job lasted for just over two months when I was offered the job where I currently work.

I worked for 23 years with the State Department of Health. The name of my particular bureau was called, Children with Special Health Care Needs. It was the Title V: Maternal Child Health program for my state. The department oversaw many programs coordinating ongoing care for children who received services. We diagnosed children with special health care needs with direct services. We worked toward helping families obtain private insurance or Medicaid to pay for services. We also assisted individuals with special health care needs to transition to adult health care, work, and independence.

Specifically, we had programs to provide diagnostic services for developmental delays in children. These programs are as follows:

The Neonatal Follow Up Program was for infants who have been in the neonatal intensive care units (NICU) in hospitals. We had clinics to track and evaluate these children with a team of pediatric developmental specialists, psychologists, an ophthalmologist (eye surgeon), neurologist, audiologist, speech pathologist, nutritionist, and me, the social worker. These children were followed at this clinic until two and a half years or, in some cases, until they were four and a half.

We also had a division called Children's Hearing and Speech Services. Children were assessed by audiologists (hearing specialists) and speech pathologists to see if they had problems in these areas. When needed, we referred families to those who provided therapy.

For many years, I was part of what we called the Oro-facial Team which consisted of a plastic surgeon, orthodontist, otolaryngologist (ear nose and throat, doctor), speech pathologist, audiologist, and social worker. This program saw children with cleft lip and palate, or other related problems of the head especially the face, mouth, nose, and ears.

Our main program took several providers to six sites throughout the state to evaluate and follow children with special health care needs. We flew to these locations, which got us to any part of the state in just over an hour. These were two-day clinics and most are held three times per year. We took with us two pediatricians, two psychologists, a neurologist, geneticist, speech pathologist, audiologist, occupational therapist, and/or a physical therapist, dietician, and social worker. We worked closely together in countless staff meetings discussing the needs of our patients and the necessary follow up with local health department nurses and staff. We also had an orthopedic clinic (muscle and bone surgeons) which traveled to these same sites twice a year.

One of the major responsibilities we faced at these clinics was to diagnose children with Autism Spectrum Disorders. These evaluations were done by our psychologists, and they were overwhelmed with the number of requests for autism testing.

My Responsibility with These Clinics

I also performed ADHD evaluations and met with the families of these children to refer them to any local or other resources. Some of these resources are as follows: Supplemental Security Income or SSI, Medicaid, foundations and support groups for all kinds of special needs, local therapists of all kinds from medical therapy to mental health, early intervention services, respite care, where to get help for IEPs and 504 plans for children in school, as well as transition services for children as they go into adulthood. In addition, I gave these good parents the time they needed to unload their burdens, to cry, or to just let them talk about anything on their minds. Many were overwhelmed with the responsibilities of caring for a child with special needs, and they needed someone to listen. For several years, I worked closely with a pediatric neurologist who required that I be with her during each of her appointments. She asked me to run a support group for parents who had children with epilepsy, which I did for over two years. I am grateful for all I learned from her and the amazing parents and patients we served.

I have a part-time private therapy practice in my home office, wherein I see people with depression, anxiety, phobias, grief, victims of abuse and various other problems. I essentially deal with any issue except drugs and alcohol use/abuse and more serious mental-emotional problems that require hospitalization. I also do marriage counseling.

I have been doing part time therapy at an OB/GYN clinic for over 21 years, and I see many patients with all kinds of concerns. For about two years, at the request of the doctor who owned the clinic, I ran a support group for women who had postpartum blues or postpartum depression. Today, I see many women who are struggling with this problem.

I have performed adoption home studies for 39 years since starting my career with the first agency I worked with. Back in the late 1990s, I served on the board of directors for an international adoption agency and, after a couple of years in this position, I was asked to assume the role of Director of Social Work for the agency. After a two-year absence I am back as the full time Director of Social Work. I began doing international adoption studies and over the years much has changed, especially since the United States implemented The Hague Convention for international adoptions. This has been good and bad and it has been costly and difficult for agencies to comply with. I have also served in the same capacity as Director of Social Work for a small domestic adoption agency.

The Voice

About 30 years ago I was reading a book on self-defeating behaviors and a very clear voice sad to me, "When are you going to write your book?" I was taken back because this was a very surreal experience and it hit me with a calm yet powerful impact. I thought to myself, "What would I write a book about?" I really believed I had nothing significant to offer, yet I could never really shake this persistent impression over the years, until I had the strong feeling that I needed to start writing.

As I began to consider what I would write I realized that I had been given a multitude of professional and other experiences that might help individuals and families who are in need of some guidance and direction. I started to write and found that the list of subjects I had strong feelings about were many. I was really very surprised as I formulated this list and I became converted to the fact that there are a lot of things to be said that the general public needs to hear. During this process, I have felt a drive to complete this task, it was strong and constant and I believe it has come from a higher power. I would have rather skated along and taken it easy rather than write this book, because that is my nature. I have found that I am definitely not a writer and this entire process has been difficult to stay focused on. Yet, I kept saying to that voice inside my head, "Okay, Okay I'll get back to it," many more times than I could count. I hope I have accomplished this goal and that you might find something in these books that will make a difference in your life.

chapter two

THE HEALING PROCESS

People do not generally understand how they can get over the damage caused by years of abuse, neglect, or feelings of insignificance, depression, anxiety, etc. I have created an explanation of how healing takes place within therapy and I call it the Healing Process.

The illustration in Figure 1 depicts what we call a volcano, but what we see is only the cone or the cooled remains of what a volcano really is, which is deep beneath the ground. The molten rock, has been pushed up to the surface. Everything above ground is similar to our conscious mind or the things we see, are aware of, and talk about in our environment. The active, dynamic part of the volcano is deep underground and cannot be seen, but we know it is there with heat and pressure which can build up and push lava through to the surface at any time. This volcano under the surface is similar to the subconscious mind. We are motivated by our subconscious mind to act in various ways each day. These forces in our lives are a product of all of the experiences we have in life.

Let me explain. Have you ever had difficulty doing something because of a fear or phobia? This could be a fear of speaking in front of people or wanting to tell someone how you feel about him or her. You decide how you are going to deal with this anxious situation, and you might even practice what you will say. Then, when you get to the

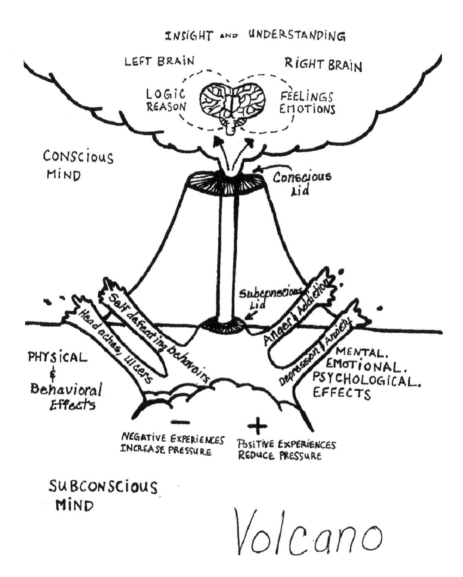

Figure 1 Illustration by Matt Anderson

actual moment, you do something else instead. You say to yourself, "I can't believe I didn't do what I had planned." The reason you didn't is because your subconscious is much more in charge than you think it is because it wants to protect you from possible harm. Consciously you are thinking you will do one thing and your subconscious says, "No, you're not."

All our experiences, whether good or bad, are stored in our subconscious mind. The negative memories cause pressure to build up and the positive ones help to reduce this pressure. The problem is if these negative memories from our subconscious are not resolved, they can cause more inner conflict as the pressure increases. The way to reduce pressure in the subconscious is to allow these memories and conflicts to come to the surface into the conscious mind so they can be resolved. The trouble here is that the subconscious mind has a job to do and that job is to protect us from these memories that are painful. In order to do so it puts a lid over them at the subconscious level and buries them deeper into the subconscious to keep the conscious mind from being aware of them. What this does over time is to cause more pressure and stress to build. Eventually these memories begin to make it to the conscious mind through flashbacks, dreams, or being exposed to something that triggers a memory.

When our conscious mind becomes aware of these troublesome memories, we consciously place a lid on them because we don't want to deal with them either, again causing more pressure to develop. If we don't relieve the pressure by addressing them, they can push to the surface in counterproductive ways. As you will note in the volcano depiction, when the lava cannot escape through the main vent the pressure causes it to break out to the surface through fissures or cracks in the surface. When this happens, these problems can be manifested physically with headaches, ulcers, or other related physical problems. They also cause mental-emotional problems like depression, anxiety, posttraumatic stress disorder, and countless others. Because we have not released the stress in healthy ways the lava escapes abnormally and without processing and resolution it can cause problematic behaviors like, angry and abusive behavior, drug and alcohol abuse, criminal behavior, physical symptoms, isolating one's self, and many others. When this happens, we can react in self-defeating ways because we have not taken the proper steps to healing.

The First Step to Healing

When we become aware that we have a problem through flashbacks, dreams, anger, depression, etc. or the manifestation of symptoms I have just described, hopefully we are ready for the first step in the healing process. What is needed to heal is to release the pressure and get the issues we have been avoiding out into our conscious awareness. This is done in a number of ways but first we must be ready to deal with these memories. That means, for most people, that we become weary of dodging the skeletons in our closets and are ready to face them. If we aren't ready to face them then we probably won't be seeking therapy because that is what we do in therapy, we deal with them. We get these issues to the surface by talking or writing how we feel about them until the stress and pressure is relieved. We can do this as we share these experiences and feelings with a trusted individual who is objective and accepts anything and everything we have to say without judging us. This is very important to have someone we can trust who will listen unconditionally. This can also be done by writing a letter to those we have issues with until, over time, we feel like we have expressed everything we feel. After reaching that point we may need to do more later on, but it won't be as difficult to do. This letter may never be sent and can just be torn up or burned depending on what the person wants to do when he or she is finished. We can also use a method called the, "Empty Chair Technique." This involves talking to someone we have issues with as if he or she is in front of us in an empty chair. This is another appropriate method of getting rid of resentment, anger, or any other feelings we have toward the person/persons or situation. In this controlled setting, we can say anything we want, and it is important to say how we feel with the same intensity as it is felt inside. For example, if you say you are upset with someone, and you actually are furious or enraged then those feelings are still being stuffed down in our conscious or subconscious and aren't getting to the surface. They are also not totally honest feelings because you are holding back. In order to do this and let it all out, I have had clients who have gone home and chopped wood, hit a couch cushion with a baseball bat, beat up a pillow or gone outside and yelled how they felt. Another method I use to accomplish this is to teach the client relaxation exercises and when a pleasant level of relaxation has been achieved I have him or her see a calm place in the mind that is safe and peaceful. Then I have him or her visualize a chair and instruct the client to place a person they need to talk to in the chair. They can say and do anything they want to that person for as long as needed, and when they are through they feel much better, having let go and said and done what they have wanted to, sometimes for the first time in their lives. They can then go back and do more of this work until they feel they have said and done everything they needed to. As these feelings and emotions are brought up from the subconscious into the conscious mind and expressed, they are felt and experienced in the right side of the brain. This can be difficult and it may feel to some that they are experiencing the pain all over again. However, remember this! The more this is done the less power it has over us to cause pain and all the other symptoms we experienced before doing this!

Right Brain, Left Brain

For years many mental health professionals have believed in the separate functions of the right and left brain. Recent studies have called into question the validity of the roles of the right and left brain as I describe it here. However, I believe to view the brain into two separate functions remains valuable in the process of helping people recover from mental and emotional injuries. That being said, I will describe the left and right brain theory as I have done so for many years.

To have mental-emotional healing, we need to involve both sides of the brain. The right side of the brain is where we experience emotions and feelings. People who experience various mental-emotional problems are usually stuck in the right brain and have trouble making sense of their world. Their right brain is so much in charge they have difficulty employing their left brain which is the center of logic and reason. It is like the right side of their brain is a large balloon and the left side is small because it is like a muscle that has become weak through lack of use. What we have to do is to let the air out of the right side by letting out all of the negative feelings and pumping up the right side by using logic and reason to bring insight and understanding to your experiences and feelings. We need to make the left side larger and more dominant until the time we are able to be more rational and objective when we have achieved balance with both sides of our brain. This is depicted in the illustration above the volcano. We bravely let out the feelings into our consciousness and as we do this we process this information with the help of the therapist to understand that what we have experienced is actually normal human reactions to our circumstances. We aren't really crazy we are responding as anyone would under the same experiences. (I am ruling out here those individuals with severe mental illness). To do this, most types of therapy utilize cognitive or thinking therapies, engaging the left brain to help balance the right brain, which has become too dominant. I am going to restate what I have just said in a different way because I want to make clear this very important point. As indicated, when a person begins to talk about his or her feelings it will be experienced in the right brain. Continuing to face and discuss these feelings and emotions reduces the power these feelings and memories have over them. As this happens and they learn more in therapy, their left brain engages and they begin to get insights and understanding about how they came to the point where they needed therapy. With these new insights, and the cognitive/thinking skills taught in therapy they become strong and more left-brained as they learn how to avoid going down the same road in the future. They learn the skills to deal with future problems.

Star Trek and Right and Left Brains

I like to tell my clients how the original characters from Star Trek demonstrate right and left brain theory. If you have ever seen the original Star Trek series you know Dr. McCoy or, "Bones," as he was called, Mr. Spock, and Captain Kirk. Dr. McCoy is the perfect example of a right brain person because he was always emotional. He almost never smiled and was always a grouch, complaining that they weren't going to survive their difficult situations, and he belittled Mr. Spock because he had no feelings. Mr. Spock is the perfect example of a left brain person because he was half Vulcan, and Vulcans do not have feelings. He was always very cerebral and would tell others if they were not being logical, i.e. "Captain that is not logical." Captain Kirk was the kind of person who could go back and forth between his right brain (feelings and emotions) and his left brain (logic and reason). He would be the one who would usually find the way out of each life threatening circumstance because he would follow his hunches which Mr. Spock did not think were logical or wise. He could out logic Spock at critical moments as well.

My point here is when we are having problems we are probably acting emotionally like Dr. McCoy. In therapy we need to learn how to think and act logically like Mr. Spock; our goal is to eventually be like Captain Kirk who maintained a balance between both right and left brains. I tell my clients while they are learning how to use their left brain they need to grow pointed ears like Mr. Spock and become a Vulcan. Live Long and Prosper!

Insight and Understanding Comes from Using Both Sides of Our Brain

When we are struggling with life the right side of our brain is much larger than our left brain because it is full of strong emotions, overwhelming our left brain or logic and reason. We need to express our emotions as I have explained by releasing the feelings and emotions much like letting out the air from a balloon. At the same time, we increase the left side of the brain by using it, which is similar to pumping it up by adding air. This is done by stating in more objective and logical terms what is really true and accurate rather than emotional and illogical feeling statements, which cause the right brain to increase in size. This process is found in the chapter on DEPRESSION DEFINITION AND TREATMENT.

Using logic and reason creates insights and understanding as to how our right brain became overwhelmed, at the same time strengthening more logical and objective thoughts. When we get to this point we are on our way to healing as we stay on task.

Releasing feelings and emotions causes the right brain to decrease in size. Using logic and reason causes the left brain to enlarge creating insights and understanding as to how our right brain became overwhelmed, causing our distorted thinking.

The Healing Process

Physical Healing	Mental/Emotional/Spiritual Healing
• Injury	• Injury
• Pain	• Pain
• Bleeding	• Bleeding
• First Aid	• Support/Therapy/Medication
• Healing	• Healing

The Physical and Mental/Emotional/Spiritual Healing Process

Now that we have discussed the volcano, let's tie those concepts into the Healing Process so that this all makes sense. At the bottom of the illustration above you will see the Physical & Mental/Emotional/Spiritual Healing Process. Let's look at the Physical side first. When a person has a physical injury, he or she needs to do a few things for healing to take place. Pretend you are walking along a beach, knee deep in the water, and you step on a broken bottle causing a large gash in your foot. The first thing you experience is pain. This pain is good because it lets you know that something is wrong. At the same time, you start to bleed, putting you at risk. Because of the pain we know we have an injury, so we look and see that we are bleeding. This prompts us to obtain medical care and with the proper treatment, over time, we heal.

What would happen if you did not have pain or you ignored the pain? You would continue to bleed and possibly pass out from loss of blood, leading to death or you might even drown. The point here is that pain is very important to the healing process because it informs us that something is very wrong and medical attention is needed.

The mental/emotional/spiritual healing process is similar, and when we have been injured in one or more of these ways, whether it be depression, abuse, or any other possible diagnosis, we experience pain. What do most people do with this mental/emotional/spiritual pain? We ignore it, minimize it and try not to let anyone know about it. What are the consequences? We continue to have pain and we bleed mentally, emotionally, and spiritually. I think the description of bleeding is very descriptive of what people go through as they agonize over unresolved mental/emotional/spiritual injuries and pain. If we do not get first aid for these injuries as with physical injuries, there can be serious consequences. What is first aid for these types of injuries? The answer is counseling or therapy, both terms mean the same thing. Therefore, a very important part of the healing process is pain because it is what motivates us to action to stop the bleeding and get the first aid/therapy we need so healing may begin.

What is the Next Step?

Now that I have explained how the process of healing takes place the next thing to do is get help from a professional to assist you through this process. People can try doing this on their own but it is much more difficult to accomplish. This is why having someone who is trained in diagnosing and implementing the correct treatment is crucial in the healing process. Depression, abuse, anxiety and many other difficult problems require different approaches for effective treatment. If anyone is struggling with an issue I would encourage that person to contact a therapist and make an appointment for an assessment. An assessment is important so the therapist can determine how severe the problem is, what the diagnosis is and what the treatment plan will be. If you are fortunate and your symptoms are minor, you may only require a session or two and further therapy may not be required. If this is the case, you may come away with confidence that you can deal with your concern on your own with a few recommendations from the therapist. Others may need more sessions because their symptoms might be more serious. I have mentioned in another chapter that I normally see clients from 3 to 8 sessions with 5 being the average. This is the estimate for those who are not experiencing severe mental illness.

I hope this helps you to understand how we heal from our painful life experiences in therapy and to understand that by ignoring them we prolong needless suffering. There are many self-help books and workbooks which can be useful for some people and situations that are mild in severity. They teach methods and strategies for dealing with many kinds of personal challenges. However, always be aware that there is no substitute for seeing a competent professional.

Severe Mental Disorders

For those individuals who have severe mental illness, i.e. schizophrenia, bipolar disorder and many others, they will require specialized treatment from psychiatrists with medication and therapists. These are often lifelong disorders and require constant monitoring of medications and behaviors. Families with loved ones who have these diagnoses will need to be supportive and understanding toward the person all the while feeling frustrated and hopeless at times about the family member. Often the family believes if the diagnosed person would just stop being lazy and get a job that everyone would be happy. It is just not that simple. Education to understand more fully the lives of these struggling individuals is highly important. I recommend that every family who has someone with a severe diagnosis attend a 12-week class called Family to Family Education Program through NAMI, the National Alliance on Mental Health. You will learn about common reactions to having a family member with chronic mental illness, goals for that family member, understanding schizophrenia and mood disorders and many other diagnoses such as posttraumatic stress disorder, borderline personality disorder and many others, basics about the brain, problem solving, medications and how they work, understanding what it is like to live with a brain disorder and developing empathy for the individual, communication skills, self-care for the family, what recovery is and rehabilitation programs, dealing with stigma and sharing the experience of living with a person with mental illness.

Usually these groups are held in conjunction with another group for the individuals with a diagnosis to assist them in adapting to life and family. That program is called Bridges which helps the mentally ill person learn coping skills and to develop relationship with others who struggle with similar diagnoses so they have support and realize they are not alone. These classes are found literally everywhere across the nation. Your local mental health center is a usually a good place to find these classes.

NAMI has many other programs for teens and young adults, veterans and active duty personnel, LGBTQ and diverse communities. Their current website is www.nami.org. I cannot stress enough the importance of reaching out and becoming involved with NAMI. I sincerely believe you will be very happy if you do and you will come away with a feeling of gratitude and understanding. Simply put, you will be in a better place feeling more prepared and stronger to deal with a loved one who has mental illness.

chapter three

ANXIETY DEFINITION AND TREATMENT

Anxiety is the most common condition I see in my practice today. It has many faces and needs to be understood by everyone because it will most likely impact every family in some way. No one really understands why so many people, especially youth, experience anxiety today. There are a number of theories including the notion that in this age of high speed information there is so much data we have to process that it is much like trying to drink from a fire hose. It can't be done because of too much pressure and no way to process the information as quickly as it is perceived by the brain. Hopefully, someday we will understand why this is happening.

Anxiety Defined

Anxiety is not easily defined because it takes so many forms. We could say that in general, anxiety involves fears or phobias and what symptoms a person experiences when these fears are present. Let's look at them one at a time.

Social Phobia

This is a severe and constant fear of doing something in front of people that might be embarrassing or humiliating, causing the person extreme distress. Just thinking about being in a social situation can cause him or her to have a panic attack, described later in this chapter. The person knows the fear is extreme and not logical; however, despite this he or she cannot overcome the anxiety and agony felt; therefore, every effort is made to avoid social situations. This can cause all kinds of problems in every aspect of the person's life.

Obsessive Compulsive Disorder

Obsessive thoughts can be simply defined by something children do as they walk along a sidewalk, "Step on a crack, break your mother's back." So what do the children do? They avoid stepping on a crack. What does that do? It reduces the anxiety from the original thought because they avoid breaking their mother's back. The compulsive act reduces the stress and worry over the obsessive thought, and that is why it is called Obsessive Compulsive Disorder. This starts with an obsessive thought that causes stress, and in order to stop the stress, the person does something compulsive he or she thinks will stop the stress. Some kids or adults take this to an extreme and will literally avoid anything they start obsessing over.

These obsessive thoughts are real life conditions not just worries. These people know that they themselves are causing these unreasonable, obsessive thoughts. They also know that they are excessive, and they try to rid their minds of them. The compulsive acts can be either behaviors or thoughts. Hand washing is common as well as counting or saying words or phrases over and over. These behaviors or phrases meant to stop the obsessive thoughts are not logical or realistic, and at some point in time they recognize this truth.

Posttraumatic Stress Disorder

You have heard about this diagnosis with regard to veterans who have returned from combat experiences. People who have been victims of violent crimes, physical or sexual abuse, valid threats, or natural disasters may also experience Posttraumatic Stress Disorder. The symptoms are more pronounced when they are caused by people.

The symptoms of posttraumatic stress disorder are excessive fear and memories of the traumatic events from flashbacks or dreams to the point that it may feel like the situation is happening again. The person can have severe reactions when experiencing something that is a reminder of the distressing event. Therefore, he or she avoids thoughts, places, memories, people or anything that might trigger these memories.

Such people may not be able to remember some of what happened to them, and they may feel isolated, unable to have feelings of love or closeness to others. They may even feel like their life will not be long nor will they be able to reach their goals. They may not want to do things that used to bring them joy. Their sleep can be affected, and their moods may become difficult to live with. They may startle easily and expect something bad to happen at any time.

There is another very similar type of anxiety that is called Acute Stress Disorder, with basically the same symptoms from each category of PTSD. The difference between the two is a much shorter time frame with Acute Stress Disorder. The symptoms begin within 4 weeks of a traumatic event and lasts between three days to 4 weeks. PTSD lasts longer causing much more distress for the individual.

Generalized Anxiety Disorder or GAD

People with Generalized Anxiety Disorder cannot control excessive worry. They are restless, become tired easily, find it hard to concentrate and sleep, and can be irritable and tense. They also worry about having a panic attack or other problems. This worry affects most areas of their lives.

Separation Anxiety

This is anxiety over being separated from home, people, or family, which can be from mild worry to extreme anxiety.

Panic Disorder, Panic Attack or Anxiety Attack

These terms are used interchangeably so don't become confused about their use. A panic attack can happen without warning and usually reaches a peak within 10 minutes. Most panic attacks end within 20 to 30 minutes, and they rarely last more than an hour. A panic attack may include a combination of the following symptoms:

- Shortness of breath or hyperventilation
- Racing heart
- Chest pain or discomfort
- Trembling or shaking
- Choking feeling
- Feeling unreal or detached from your surroundings
- Sweating
- Nausea or upset stomach
- Feeling dizzy, light-headed, or faint
- Numbness or tingling sensations
- Hot or cold flashes
- Fear of dying, losing control, or going crazy

Physically speaking this is the worst of the anxiety disorders, and it usually causes great distress and more worry about having another episode. It is very common for someone who has experienced a panic attack to think they are having a heart attack. Many of these people end up in the emergency room and after blood tests and a heart monitor test referred to as an Electrocardiogram (EKG or ECG) they are cleared of heart problems. At this point the person is diagnosed with panic disorder and is referred for treatment to any or all of the following: the primary care physician, a psychiatrist for medication, or a psychotherapist.

Diagnosis

As in depression and other diagnoses the following is a basic description of how therapy starts and progresses with regard to anxiety. The first session or diagnostic evaluation begins by asking the client why they have come to therapy and what they hope to accomplish. This is called identifying the presenting problem. Next is a review of the history of any other problems and previous therapy experiences. Identifying the family history of mental-emotional diagnoses is also important to understand other factors contributing to the problem.

At this point the client is given the opportunity to say what is on his or her mind. Other questions are asked to clarify what he or she is saying or feeling. We narrow down the symptoms the person is experiencing to come up with a workable diagnosis of the problem.

If I have a client who I believe has anxiety, after reviewing their symptoms, I ask questions to determine how severe the anxiety is. If it is severe enough I will discuss with him or her the possible need for medications and describe how they work. We also discuss how to access a doctor who can prescribe medication.

Treatment

Once a diagnosis has been identified, I create a treatment plan for the client. Therapy for anxiety or any other problem involves understanding, education, and insight. Understanding the client leads to a diagnosis of the problem; we then focus on educating the client, after which we work on coping skills and greater insight into his or her situation and how to avoid anxiety in the future.

Some anxiety is caused by difficult experiences as described above. Panic Disorder is often something that shows up out of the blue with no warning and no precipitating events. It just happens! Some people are predisposed to it genetically because of a family history of anxiety, and others may not have such a family history. It is not totally understood why Panic Disorder or any other anxiety disorders happen to some and not to others.

Because anxiety is also a fear or phobia I like to read with my clients a handout with two paragraphs from the chapter on HOW WE DEVELOP OUR INDIVIDUAL IDIOSYCRACIES AND FEARS. It is from a book called, "Frogs into Princes," by Bandler and Grinder. I read this because in the case of a fear or phobia, it helps a person understand how his or her anxiety was formed. The exception to this is the case of Panic Disorder or anxiety which has occurred without an apparent reason. In such instances the cause may well be a genetic type of anxiety having no identifiable cause. The following is the quote I referred to.

"There are many, many useful ways of organizing the whole process called psychotherapy. One of the ways that is quite simple, and therefore elegant, is to treat every psychological limitation like a phobia. A person who has a phobia made a decision, unconsciously, under stress, sometime earlier in their life in the face of overwhelming stimuli. They succeeded in doing something that humans often have a hard time doing. They succeeded in one-trial learning. Every time that set of stimuli comes up again later in their life, they make exactly the same response. It's a remarkable achievement. You change over the years, and despite the external contextual changes, you are still able to maintain that stimulus-response arc.

The thing that makes phobias sort of interesting is the fact that the responses are so consistent. If a person says "I can't be assertive around my boss," they are essentially saying "somewhere in my personal history I have an experience or a set of experiences on being assertive. I cannot get to that resource in the context of my boss." When a person responds with the phobic response to a snake, that's a similar situation. I know that at other times in their experience, in their personal history, they have been able to be quite calm and courageous. However, in the context of a snake, they can't get to that resource." [1]

---

1   Bandler, R. and Grinder, J. (1979). *Frogs into Princes: Neuro Linguistic Programming,* P. 109. Lafayette, CA: Real People Press.

I tell my clients that when we acquire these fears, often at an early age, we take them into adulthood with us. We just get taller and older but we bring along these fears we learn as a child. Most of the time these fears are not logical, and the person realizes this is true.

After reading this quote to one of my clients, she recalled at the age of 14 exactly what happened when her phobia began. She was offered a babysitting job one night a week on Wednesdays. Soon after accepting this job she said to herself, "What if I want to do something else on that night, what will I do?" This caused her to feel anxiety as she worried about what she would do if something else came up she would rather do. From that time forth, when she found herself in a tightly structured schedule or environment she became anxious and fought to keep herself from feeling out of control, even somewhat claustrophobic. She is now an adult and found herself committed to a situation where her time and schedule was highly structured seven days a week. She began having debilitating anxiety and, after a month, she woke up one day with depression, realizing she needed to remove herself from her current stressful environment and return to what she was doing previously. She was worried she might have more anxiety because she had not finished the assignment she had desired to complete. I took her through the following process.

Systematic Desensitization

I explained to her that some years ago I had a mother bring in her 13-year old daughter who had separation anxiety. Whenever her parents left home she was sure they were going to be killed in an auto accident. She became frantic when they would leave, and her anxiety became so excessive that her mother knew she needed help. After diagnosing her condition, I explained how we needed to help her become aware of when her anxious feelings begin to take hold of her. If she can identify them before they get to a five on a scale of zero to ten in terms of anxiety, then it is much easier to cope with them using cognitive therapy techniques. One of these skills is called systematic desensitization. This is a process of learning how to completely relax and then to introduce the anxiety provoking thoughts or feelings gradually until the person is able to visualize an anxious situation without becoming overwhelmed.

I asked her to close her eyes and tell me what she was feeling inside and to rate how strong her feelings were on a scale of zero to ten, ten being the strongest and zero being relaxed and almost asleep. She was nervous at about a seven or eight. I guided this young woman through a number of exercises which have the effect of relaxing and calming someone to the point of almost putting him or her to sleep. Her mother was there, and I asked her to pay attention so she could talk her through this same process each evening at home. By the end of our session she was able to get herself to a very calm and peaceful state, and she was able to visualize a very safe and beautiful place in her mind that she would go to when she was practicing this skill. Her assignment was to work with her mother as a team to become good at getting to a relaxed state.

The following week she came back, after working each night to get her relaxation skills where she was able to get to a one or zero quite well. I took her through the same process again and asked her to see her safe place. When this was done I asked her to visualize her parents getting ready to leave the house. She saw her mother doing her hair, putting on her makeup, leaving the house, driving off and coming back safe and sound. She was to begin this process until she found herself becoming anxious and before she reached a five on the anxious scale she was to stop the video in her mind and go back to deep breathing or one of the other skills that caused her to relax until she returned to a one or zero and then she was to go back to her video and press the play button where she was before she pressed the stop button. Her instructions were to continue to repeat this process until she was able to get through the entire scenario with her parents returning safely. I had her repeat this a few times and then instructed her and her mother to repeat this daily as often as possible during the following week.

They returned the next week and had practiced this skill many times. I took her through the process again and asked this young girl how she felt when she thought of her parents leaving home, and she was happy to report that she did not fear this scene anymore. She hardly had any feelings at all about her parents leaving. Essentially, she had repeated the exercise enough that she had become desensitized to this previously paralyzing situation.

A year later her mother brought her younger sister to see me with exactly the same problem. I met with her and her mother twice, with her mother helping during the week as she had with the older sister and by the second session she was anxiety free. Approximately a year later the older sister came back again because she was having anxiety about going to girls' camp. I met with her once taking her through the relaxation and visualization of going to camp, and I never saw either of them again.

This process of systematic desensitization works well with most of the anxiety disorders. It is more difficult to cope with an all-out panic or anxiety attack because it can be so debilitating and overwhelming. It is still very helpful to learn the relaxation and visualization skills because it is a valuable tool in battling these overpowering bouts of anxiety.

A person with a history of panic attacks can work at desensitization between attacks and can greatly increase his or her ability to cope when it happens. When a person becomes aware that a panic attack is imminent he or she can utilize relaxation skills and possibly some desensitization; however, he or she will probably not be able to completely shut down the experience. With skills acquired in therapy he or she will be better able to reduce certain aspects of the attack. To more fully reduce the physical effects of panic attacks taking an antianxiety medication can make all the difference in diminishing the symptoms.

Exercise

There have been many studies over the years indicating the importance of regular exercise to help with anxiety or any mental-emotional problem. The common recommendation is to have at least three cardiovascular workouts of 20 minutes or more per week. The benefits of exercise are numerous and can make such a difference in a person's emotional well-being. Exercise improves self-esteem, reduces stress, reduces anxiety and depression, produces a feeling of well-being and improves sleep. It also has a host of other physical benefits such as more energy, stronger muscles and bones, less body fat and lower levels of blood pressure and cholesterol. There are chemicals in the brain called endorphins that are produced with regular exercise that give a person a feeling of well-being. There is no question that regular exercise will help with the treatment of anxiety.

Medications for Anxiety

There are a couple of classifications of medicines that are most common in helping people with anxiety. SSRIs are discussed in the chapter on MEDICATIONS FOR MENTAL HEALTH TREATMENT. These types of medications are taken daily and are referred to as prophylactic because they are meant to treat the problem by keeping it from starting up. The other type is referred to as benzodiazepines and are used as a prophylactic or as something to take when anxiety or a panic attack is coming on or has begun. This second type is faster acting and that is why they can be taken when a person feels anxiety coming on.

Self-Talk and the Left and Right Brain

I discuss self-talk using left and right brain theory in chapters on THE HEALING PROCESS and DEPRESSION DEFINITION AND TREATMENT. Self-talk is using logic and reason to fight off the cognitive distortions we develop in life. In the chapter on depression I have included Dr. David Burns' 10 Cognitive Distortions, found is his book, "Feeling Good The New Mood Therapy," and I often use them when treating someone with anxiety to get the patient using logic and reason to overcome debilitating negative feelings and thoughts. This is the essence of self-talk, to give the person the verbal ammunition to become more objective and reasonable when dealing with illogical thoughts and feelings. When used consistently, this becomes an empowering tool to recognize and better control anxious thoughts and feelings.

Self-talk begins with people learning how to tune into their body and mind in order to be aware when they are just starting to feel anxiety or thinking in negative terms. When people catch themselves before these feelings or thoughts reach a five on a scale of zero to ten, they will say, "Stop. Think. What am I doing? I am starting to feel or say distortions about myself and that will lead me to feeling anxious and overwhelmed." Such persons then begin saying objective defensive statements which they have prepared in advance in order to counter their distorted thinking with logical, objective statements. Thus, you have self-talk referred to now days as a form of self-regulation.

The result of this self-talk is shifting from overwhelming feelings, a right brain function to the left brain where logic and reason resides. We all do this with children, loved ones, friends, and those in our extended world when we are attempting to encourage them and help them to see that life is not as bad as they are feeling. The trick is to apply this strategy to ourselves to bring more objective and rational thoughts into our consciousness. This is how we conquer these deflating, anxious, and fearful emotions.

These are just a few of the methods professionals use to assist their clients to cope with panic attack and the various forms of anxiety. I hope this discussion will help those who fight these difficult feelings to seek professional help. There is hope and healing with a good therapist.

There are a number of workbooks I refer patients to when working with anxiety. The one I use most often is called "The Anxiety and Phobia Workbook," by Edmund J. Bourne Ph.D. I believe such workbooks are excellent supplements to psychotherapy. Be aware that with any mental-emotional challenge a person may have to go back for what I call a refresher session or more after he or she has successfully completed therapy. This may happen a few months or even years later and is common so don't be surprised if that becomes necessary. Good luck!

chapter four

DEPRESSION DEFINITION AND TREATMENT

By addressing this issue, I hope to give the general public a basic understanding of what depression is and how it is treated. It has been treated with success for many years using several proven methods. There is no need to suffer from depression, it is treatable and for many who don't have more serious forms, hope and recovery can be just weeks away.

When I first started doing therapy, depression was the most common problem I saw in my practice. Over the years it has taken a bit of a backseat to anxiety, which is the most common problem I see today. Depression and Anxiety are often found together in patients.

Depression is a form of sadness that goes beyond just feeling discouraged. The symptoms are listed here and they must be present for at least 2 weeks in order to diagnose someone with depression:

- Feeling sad most days of the week

- No pleasure or interest in things they used to enjoy

- No appetite or eating too much, weight loss or gain

- Lack of sleep or sleeping too much

- Trouble getting started on tasks or feelings of agitation

- No energy

- Feeling no sense of worth or guilt feelings

- Thoughts of death or even suicide

Having 5 of the above symptoms would qualify a person for the diagnosis of what is called Major Depression. A person with Minor Depression would have less than 5 of the symptoms and unless treated they may develop Major Depression.

Other Depression Diagnoses

• There are also other less common forms of depression, which can be severe. Some of these are;

• Postpartum depression after giving birth which is more severe than the baby blues.

• Dysthymic disorder or dysthymia which is depression of two years or longer.

• Psychotic depression causing delusions or hallucinations.

• Seasonal affective disorder or SAD, which is depression during winter months when less sunlight is present.

• Bipolar disorder or manic depression where the person's mood, cycles between highs and lows.

How Severe is the Depression?

There are physical symptoms and mental/emotional symptoms. The following is a list of these symptoms from minor to more severe forms of depression. I came across this list some years ago with no reference to who created it. I believe it applies in determining how severe depression is and when medication might be required to help a person return to a higher level of functioning.

Physical Symptoms	**Mental-Emotional Symptoms**

(Symptoms are minor from top to severe at bottom)

• Loss or increase of appetite	• Pessimism
• Insomnia	• Discouragement
• Fatigue	• Loss of Interest
• Aches and Pains	• Low Self-Esteem
• Decreased Self-Care	• Low Confidence
• Purposeless Activity	• Unhappiness
• Slow Speech	• Crying Spells
• Unable to Make Decisions	• Slow Physical Activity
	• Slow Thinking
	• Difficulty Focusing
	• Irritability
	• Poor Memory
	• Poor Judgment
	• Fearfulness
	• Thoughts of Death
	• Self-Depreciation
	• Hopelessness
	• Feeling Worthless and Guilty
	• Plans of Suicide
	• Withdrawal
	• Delusional Thoughts
	• Preparing for Suicide

These symptoms of depression are cause for greater concern and may need more aggressive treatment with therapy and medication.

Symptoms

- Sleep Disturbance
- No Emotion also called Flat Affect
- Appetite Disturbance
- Agitation
- Inability to Feel Pleasure
- Slowed Body Movements called
- Fatigue
- Psychomotor Retardation
- Decreased Libido

History

- No Precipitating Events
- Cyclic Moods
- Family History of
- Depression
- Suicide
- Highs of mood
- Alcoholism

If someone has several of these symptoms they should be evaluated by a psychiatrist who is best trained to treat patients with medications. Refer to the short chapter on MEDICATION FOR MENTAL HEALTH TREATMENT to understand how medication may be necessary for treatment. Briefly put here, it may be necessary for someone who is severely depressed to benefit from medication in order to increase the level of function so they can apply the concepts below in order to recover more fully and in a timely manner. Otherwise they may suffer longer and deeper depression unnecessarily.

Diagnosis

The following is a basic description of how therapy starts and progresses. Therapy begins by asking the client why they have come to therapy and what they hope to accomplish. This is called identifying the presenting problem. Next is a review of the history of any other problems and previous therapy experiences. Identifying the family history of mental, emotional diagnoses is also important to understand other factors contributing to the problem.

At this point the client is given the opportunity to say what is on his or her mind and sometimes this goes for a while. Other questions may be asked to clarify what he or she is saying or feeling. Then we begin to get closer to what the problem is and narrow down the symptoms the person is experiencing to come up with a workable diagnosis of the problem.

If I have clients who I believe have Major Depression, after reviewing their symptoms, I will give them a questionnaire to help determine how severe the depression is. If it is severe enough I will discuss with them the possible need for medications and describe how they work. We also discuss how to access a doctor who can prescribe medication. I determine if grief is part of the picture and if it is I discuss the stages of grief found in the chapter on the same subject in this book. I then explain the 3 different kinds of depression listed below.

Treatment

Therapy for depression involves understanding, education and insight. Understanding the client's feelings and emotions leads to a diagnosis of the problem, educating the client, and working on coping skills and greater insight into their situation and how to avoid depression in the future.

3 Types of Depression

1) Situational or Reactive: This is when a person encounters a situation in life where they have a loss or challenge they cannot control. They react to the situation with some or many of the above symptoms. This can be caused by death, divorce or any other problem that is stressful. With this kind of depression there is an identifiable cause.

2) Neurotic or Cognitive: This is caused by the way the person thinks. They may have experienced Situational depression for a period of time that leads to this Cognitive or Thinking depression. Their thinking becomes so confused that they have difficulty being objective or logical. They think negative thoughts about themselves and may have inferior feelings, perfectionism, compulsive and worrisome thoughts.

3) Endogenous: This has a genetic, biological, chemical basis that is caused by ones predisposition to depression from their genetic makeup. This is why it is important to discuss the history of depression in the client's family.

I discuss what I think the diagnosis is and begin the first stages of the treatment plan. I then review the steps we will take to overcome the depression.

The Healing Process

In most cases at this time, I share with the patient THE HEALING PROCESS in the chapter under the same name. It would be well for you to read that chapter now or after you read this chapter. The following are methods I use to treat individuals with depression.

Exercise

Review the paragraph on Exercise in the previous chapter on Anxiety to understand the benefits of exercise for depression. Exercise should be part of any treatment plan in dealing with depression.

Expressing Feelings is Important

If the client has anger toward anyone because of how they were treated earlier in life or even currently, I want them to express their feelings. This can be done in a number of ways from writing how they feel to expressing these feelings while visualizing the person or persons in their mind. They can also do this using an empty chair in a room as they verbalize what they have wanted to say but have been reluctant or afraid to. This is something I give as an assignment to do throughout the following week using the method most comfortable for them. It is surprising how much emotion can come out during these exercises and how healing it is. If anger is not expressed it stays within the individual and affects how he or she deals with life. This is very therapeutic and frees individuals from years of pent up emotions. This may take a few sessions or several depending on the individual and how severe their feelings and even anger is. More details about this process are found in the chapter on THE HEALING PROCESS.

Low Self Esteem

Often those who have depression have low self-esteem and addressing this is critical. Many of these individuals have criticized themselves harshly for years on end. They have no balance in terms of judging who they really are objectively. In such cases I give them an assignment to ask 3 or more people they trust to write a list of positives about them. When they receive these lists they make a master list and if there are duplicate positive attributes they place an asterisk by each trait to indicate that others have identified the same positive. I ask them to read this list 10 times per day and believe it. Let it sink in. Internalize it. People who write these lists do not write false statements to make them feel better. I have found they are very honest and accurate in describing these individuals they care about. I also find that the client knows what is written is really true and it has an amazing, uplifting effect on them.

Right Brain, Left Brain

Learning to stop focusing on the negative thoughts one feels and to become objective about one's self is a powerful way to change depression. This is a method of making a person aware of their feelings and to shift gears, so to speak, from feelings and emotions, which are usually inaccurate, to logic and reason. The right brain is where we experience feelings and emotions and the left brain is where we use logic and reason. This is explained more fully in the chapter on THE HEALING PROCESS.

The 10 Cognitive Distortions

One of the therapy methods for depression that has been a staple for many years is what is called the 10 Cognitive Distortions by David D. Burns M.D. This is a method of helping a person to identify his or her thinking errors and how to rethink and avoid these errors. Dr. Burns' book, Feeling Good the New Mood Therapy, is an excellent book where these distortions and other techniques are found. Here is his list and description of these distortions with an example of a housewife who uses a number of them. Finally is Dr. Burns' example of the triple column technique which is used by clients to change their distorted thinking by utilizing self-talk when they start to engage in their cognitive distortions.

1) **All or Nothing Thinking:** You see things in black and white categories. If your performance falls short of perfect, you see yourself as a total failure.

2. **Overgeneralization:** You see a single negative event as a never-ending pattern of defeat.

3. **Mental Filter:** You pick out a single negative detail and dwell on it exclusively so that your vision of all reality becomes darkened, like the drop of ink that discolors the entire beaker of water.

4. Disqualifying the Positive: You reject positive experiences by insisting they "don't count" for some reason or other. In this way, you can maintain a negative belief that is contradicted by your everyday experiences.

5. Jumping to Conclusions: You make a negative interpretation even though there are no definite facts that convincingly support your conclusions.

- **Mind Reading.** You arbitrarily conclude that someone is reacting negatively to you, and you don't bother to check this out.

- **The Fortune Teller Error.** You anticipate that things will turn out badly, and you feel convinced that your prediction is an already established fact.

6. Magnificaation (Catastrophizing) or Minimiztion: You exaggerate the importance of things (such as your goof-up or someone else's achievement). Or you inappropriately shrink things until they appear tiny (your own desirable qualities or the other fellow's imperfections). This is also called the "binocular trick."

7. Emotional Reasoning: You assume that your negative emotions necessarily reflect the way things really are: "I feel it, therefore it must be true."

8. Should Statements: You try to motivate yourself with shoulds and shouldn'ts, as if you had to be whipped and punished before you could be expected to do anything. "Musts" and "oughts" are also offenders. The emotional consequence is guilt. When you direct should statements toward others, you feel anger, frustration, and resentment.

9. Labeling and Mislabeling: This is an extreme form of over-generalization. Instead of describing your error, you attach a negative label to yourself: "I'm a loser." When someone else's behavior rubs you the wrong way, you attach a negative label to him: "He's a louse." Mislabeling involves describing an event with language that is highly colored and emotionally loaded.

10. Personalization: You see yourself as the cause of some negative event which in fact, you were not primarily responsible for.

Dr. Burns gives an example of a housewife who uses a number of these distortions.

You are a housewife, and your heart sinks when your husband has just complained that the roast beef was overdone. The following thoughts cross your mind: "I am a total failure. I can't stand it! I never do anything right. I work like a slave and this is all the thanks I get! The jerk!" These thoughts cause you to feel sad and angry. Her distortions included, all or nothing thinking, overgeneralization, magnification and labeling.

The "triple-column technique," helps you to rethink when you have goofed up in some way. The idea is to substitute more objective and rational thoughts for the illogical, harsh self-criticisms that automatically flood your mind when a negative event occurs.

Automatic Thought/Feeling Self Criticism	Cognitive Distortion	Automatic Thought/Feeling Self Defensive Statement
I never do anything right.	Overgeneralization	Nonsense! I do a lot of things right.
I'm always late.	Overgeneralization	I'm always late. That's ridiculous. Think of all the time I have been on time. If I'm late more often than I'd like, I'll work on this and develop a method of being on time.
Everyone will look down on me.	Mind Reading Overgeneralization All-or-Nothing Thinking Fortune Teller Error	Someone may be disappointed that I'm late but it's not the end of the world. Maybe the meeting won't even start on time.
This shows what a jerk I am	Labeling	Come on, now. I'm not a jerk.
I'll make a fool of myself	Labeling Fortune Teller Error	Ditto. I'm not a fool either. I may appear foolish if I come late, but this does not make me a fool. Everyone is late sometimes.[2]

2   Burns, D. D. (1980). *Feeling Good The New Mood Therapy.* P. 33-43 & 63. New York, NY: Morrow.

You can see how identifying these distortions and then catching and correcting yourself would make big changes in someone who is hard on themselves. I have found this technique to be very effective with my clients.

When I introduce this method to a client it is remarkable how many people report doing several of these distortions. I give them the assignment to write down two or three examples of what they say to themselves for each distortion they do. Then I have them write two to three rational responses or self-defensive statements they will use when they have distorted thinking. The client's progress can be measured by having them keep track of how many distortions they have each day by recording a 1 for each distortion and then placing a circle around it for each one they have been able to stop by using the triple column technique. This is done on a piece of paper or a 3x5 card and I have found this to be an excellent measure of how well the client is progressing. Many of my patients have been surprised at how often they criticize themselves when they begin using this technique. If used over time this technique makes a huge difference for people suffering from depression as they learn how to manage their negative thinking.

There are many other skills and techniques depressed individuals can learn to assist them in recovery from depression. I have shown you a few methods I use to help these individuals and I hope it makes the decision to get help in the form of counseling less overwhelming, more appealing and less difficult.

There are many other skills and techniques depressed individuals can learn to assist them in recovery from depression. I have shown you a few methods and I hope it makes the decision to get help less overwhelming, more appealing.

chapter five

POSTPARTUM DEPRESSION

Several years ago, I was asked by an OB/GYN doctor to start a support group for women with postpartum depression. He had seen a number of patients suffering from this in his practice, and he wanted to do something about it. He asked all of his patients to attend and, despite our efforts, I ended the group after about 18 months because we could not get enough participation. I have found that getting any support group to continue is difficult and sometimes frustrating. As part of our attempt, we invited women before and after birth because depression can also happen before the birth of the child, and we wanted them to be educated to the signs and symptoms.

Since that time, I have seen many women in therapy from the same women's clinic who have experienced postpartum depression. This is a form of depression that can occur after childbirth. The strange thing is that it might occur after the birth of the first child or after any other pregnancy despite never having it before, or it may not happen at all. It can be very random and it usually takes women by surprise. I have seen women who have had four or more pregnancies with no history of depression, and suddenly it strikes without warning.

Some women experience what is called postpartum blues or the baby blues. This is the most common and least severe of postpartum problems. Estimations of how many women experience baby blues after giving birth are from 50% to 75%. The symptoms occur from two to four days after birth and can be as brief as a few hours to about a week. The symptoms may disappear quickly or gradually.

Symptoms of the Baby Blues

- Impatience
- Irritability
- Upset Feelings
- Anxiousness
- Depression
- Crying for no reason
- Restlessness
- Inability to sleep
- Eating problems
- Doubts about making choices and caring for the baby

Postpartum depression is a more serious and concerning problem requiring a visit to the doctor for an exam and diagnosis. Depending on the severity of the symptoms, it may require psychotherapy and even medication.

Symptoms of Postpartum Depression

- Feeling sad for no reason
- Exhaustion
- Loss of concentration
- Irritability
- Changes in appetite and sleep patterns
- Poor memory and concentration
- Inability to make decisions
- Lack of care and interest in the baby

• Lack of bonding to the baby despite looking forward to the birth regardless of how many other births were without problems

• Thoughts of harming self

• Fear that something bad will happen to the baby

• Fear of harming the baby

• Over concern for the baby

• Crying for no reason

• Feeling as if you are going crazy

• Lack of interest in sex

• Thoughts of death or suicide

There can be other symptoms as well, and they can appear suddenly or gradually up to a year later. This can also occur when a woman stops nursing her child so be aware that whatever triggers postpartum depression, the symptoms can be abrupt or may creep up slowly over time.

Symptoms of Postpartum Anxiety

A woman can also develop symptoms of anxiety with or without feeling depressed. This can be more common if the person has experienced anxiety prior to becoming pregnant, and the symptoms may be intensified.

• Anxiety or fear, which can be severe

• Racing or pounding heart rate

• Rapid breathing

• Stomach or chest pain

• Shaking

• Dizziness or nausea

• Panic attacks

• Sense of doom

Some women can experience Postpartum Obsessive Compulsive Disorder. As with Anxiety, if there has been a history of Obsessive Compulsive Disorder, these symptoms may be more severe.

Symptoms of Postpartum Obsessive Compulsive Disorder

• Obsessive and disturbing thoughts such as harming the baby

• Compulsive or avoiding behaviors such as staying away from the baby to decrease thoughts of harming the baby

• Anxiety

These symptoms are discussed in more detail in the chapter on ANXIETY. To be a little more descriptive, obsessive thoughts are like the example of, "Step on a crack, break your mother's back." The response to reduce the anxiety caused by these thoughts is a compulsive act such as, avoiding stepping on cracks.

Postpartum Psychosis

The most severe of the postpartum reactions is Postpartum Psychosis. This person breaks with reality and needs hospitalization and medication. This is very rare and most often the person having such a break has a history of bipolar disorder, schizophrenia or has family members with these diagnoses.

Medication may be helpful or necessary

When I meet with women suffering from postpartum depression, I try to determine how severe the condition is. I will generally give her a questionnaire with the symptoms of depression and discuss the results. If the scores are low and the depression is mild we will go on to the next step of treatment. If the condition is more serious I will talk to her about the possible use of medication. In all cases, it is important for women to get a physical exam by their doctor. As with other forms of depression, medication may be necessary for some patients until they return to a state where they can utilize the cognitive/thinking skills that I teach them to cope with their depression.

Reasons for Postpartum Depression

The reasons for these postpartum reactions are not presently known or well understood. Changing hormones because of the complex nature of pregnancy, birth, and nursing are considered the most likely causes. Corticotropin-releasing hormone or CRH is released by the hypothalamus gland which raises blood sugar levels and maintains normal blood pressure. During the last trimester of pregnancy the placenta releases CRH, in some cases to much higher levels than normal causing the hypothalamus to reduce the output of CRH. After birth and the removal of the placenta the levels of CRH can be very low as seen in people with symptoms of depression. It may take time for the hypothalamus to return to normal production of CRH. This may be one of the causes of postpartum depression, etc.

Therapy for Postpartum Depression

Many women experiencing the baby blues might only require some education, and they are on their way to recovery. If they are experiencing postpartum depression they will probably need at least one session and possibly several more. Most common in my practice I have found that the average number of appointments required is from two to three sessions for postpartum depression. With some women the symptoms linger for longer periods of time, calling for more therapy sessions.

I have found that knowledge is power when it comes to most types of therapy. Therefore, after listening to the concerns of the patient to understand what she is experiencing, I attempt to describe what I have heard her say, and when she acknowledges that I have understood what she is feeling, I give her a several page handout. As I read over this handout, with the above information, it is typical to hear a woman indicate how many of the symptoms she has or is experiencing. It is gratifying to see a woman make major shifts from thinking that she might be going crazy to a realization that all the above lists are normal for a woman who is experiencing postpartum reactions. For anyone who is going through these signs, please know that you are normal and not crazy. Yes, there are a few who need hospitalization because they might have postpartum psychosis, but the vast majority of women will get through postpartum depression with help and time. The reason the symptom lists have been created is to identify what is normal for women who are experiencing them.

After discussing these normal symptoms of postpartum depression, I teach cognitive therapy skills, or thinking therapy as I refer to it, the same as with more common depression and anxiety treatment. Simply put, cognitive therapy is a method that teaches a patient awareness of her thinking distortions and how to use logic and reason through self-talk to stop these distortions from overwhelming her. To know more about these skills, I would advise to you to read the chapters on DEPRRESSION and ANXIETY.

If you or anyone you know might be going through these symptoms you should contact your doctor for an appointment for an examination and discuss with him or her if psychotherapy is warranted. Get help and you can feel much better.

chapter six
GRIEF

Simply put, grief is our human reaction to loss of any kind. We are all different, and therefore we respond to loss quite differently. We are transferred to another department at work or a child loses a teacher when he or she goes from one grade to another. We lose our job or have to move, causing all kinds of anxiety and stress. The loss of relationships through death, divorce, or other circumstances is likely to be the most distressing to us. When a family moves, a child can become very depressed, and he or she may lose the desire to socialize. Some may even feel like they are betraying their former relationships by making new friends. Any form of loss can cause a variety of responses.

The way we respond to loss was first studied in 1942 after a fire at a nightclub in Boston that caused the death of 492 people. Because of the number of victims, there was a concerted effort to bring counselors and social workers into the community, to help the friends and families of the victims deal with this tragedy. Since that time there has been much written about grief. When people know and understand the stages of grief, they feel relieved that they are not crazy or abnormal for feeling and thinking the way they do.

The most recognized figure in describing the stages of grief is a woman by the name of Elisabeth Kubler-Ross who published her book,

On Death and Dying" [3] in 1969. She identified five stages of grief. There have been many others who have put their twists on the theme of grief since that time. I have come up with a list of seven stages of grief that I like to share with my clients. The following are Kubler-Ross's stages with the addition of some of my ideas which I share with clients. In presenting these concepts, it is important to recognize that not everyone will experience all the stages of grief, nor will they experience them in the order as listed. As you will see, grief might start immediately or it may even take months or longer for someone to begin their process of grieving. The point is that we are all different and experience grief in different ways. It can be very helpful to understand what we might go through to avoid believing that we are going crazy or are abnormal. We can also help friends and loved ones through their experiences by preparing them for the possibilities they might face. Remember, these are general guidelines which may or may not apply to everyone who has had a loss in his or her life.

7 Stages of Grief

1) Shock/Numbness/Denial

Exhaustion/Lack of patterns of conduct/Disorientation

When we first become aware of the loss we can't believe it has happened, and we struggle with the reality that faces us. Things around us seem surreal, and we can become numb emotionally, which can be interpreted by others as not caring. A person can also enter a state of denial in which he or she simply will not believe the truth. Loved ones suffering a loss may feel exhaustion or fatigue. They have difficulty conducting normal routines at work and home. In addition, they have difficulty making decisions and feel disoriented. These are all basic symptoms of situational depression.

---

3   Kubler-Ross, E. (1969). On Death and Dying. New York, NY: Scribner. ISBN 978-1-4767-7554-8.

2) Blame/Anger/Resentment/Guilt

Directed at Self/Others/God

In this stage we think, "If we hadn't done this or that, then this would not have happened, so it's my fault." This can lead to depression and self-doubt. We can become angry with someone because we blame them for the loss, which can stay in our hearts causing us to be unforgiving and resentful. We might be angry with God thinking, "If there is a God then why would he let this happen to me? Doesn't he love me anymore? Why am I being punished?"

3) Pain/Grief/Anguish

Experienced Physically/Mentally/Emotionally/Spiritually

We may experience this stage with physical pain such as headaches, stomachaches, muscle or other body pain referred to as somatic pain. Mentally we may become depressed with foggy thinking, irrational choices, feeling emotionally overwhelmed with no motivation, and other symptoms including uncontrollable crying or feeling numb and detached from reality. We may also become disenchanted with our religious beliefs and question our faith.

4) Depression

Little hope/Appetite changes/Sleep changes/Fatigue/Sadness/No enjoyment/Nothing to look forward to/Withdrawal/Thoughts of death but not necessarily with suicidal thoughts (Caution: these symptoms may or may not be experienced by those dealing with grief)

I believe it is important to include the symptoms of depression in the stages of grief because I believe depression is significant part of grief. The descriptions here are an extension of the previous stage with stronger symptoms. It can be very common for a person to feel like there is no hope. It is also common to have a lack of appetite or an increase in appetite when food becomes a comfort. Some may begin sleeping too much or they may have insomnia (the inability to sleep).

(The symptoms of situational, cognitive, and organic depression are described in the chapter dealing with depression. It would be worthwhile to review those concepts to further understand what we or our loved ones might pass through during grief. For some it may be necessary to be treated for depression if the symptoms persist and he or she is unable to resume most aspects of his or her life.)

5) Bargaining

This is when a person makes a deal with God. This can happen prior to a loss when someone suspects they are, for example, going to lose a job or a loved one and he or she says, in effect, "Okay God, if you will help me to stay employed then I will be better to my spouse or work harder at my job, or I won't drink as much, etc." This can also happen after a loss when a person might say, "If you (God) will help me get through this difficult time I will take care of my parents or promise to give to charity or give service to others, etc."

6) Acceptance

When we finally get to the point where we have gone through enough of the above stages and enough time has passed, we begin to accept the loss. This is different for every one of us and no one can tell anyone, "You should be over this by now." Be careful not to allow others to make you feel guilty. Here is where cognitive therapy can be of help as discussed in the chapter on depression. Doing some self-talk here is important. For example, say to yourself, "I have the right to deal with this at my own pace and I won't allow others to push me before I am ready."

The exception to this is if we make a conscious choice to become irresponsible and throw away all reason by giving up on life and others. If this is occurring with you or someone you love then professional help is needed. Hopefully, that person will be willing to accept help.

7) Reconciliation/Readjustment/Going on with Life

This is when we finally begin to come out of the fog, so to speak. We start feeling like ourselves and a desire to be more social and engaged in life starts to grow. We begin to experience enjoyment, fun, and happiness in ever increasing amounts. Sometimes we feel guilty for feeling happy but it is important to do some self-talk at these times and tell ourselves that we need to go on with life and our loved ones would want us to do so. We begin to redefine our world without the person or the loss, whatever it was. We can, at this juncture, find new meaning and reasons for living if we work at it.

I would like to share a personal experience on this matter. Within a two-and-a-half-month period I had a few losses. Beginning in August of 2010, my younger brother, not quite 51 years of age lost his six-and-a-half-year battle with cancer and died. My wife passed away unexpectedly in October at the age of 56, seven days after her birthday and five days prior to our 36th anniversary. Twelve days later my father died at the age of 94. Being a few years after these experiences I can say that I have been through all of the above stages. I suddenly had a desire to begin dating about nine months after my wife's death. I still can't believe at times that she is really gone, and it seems like at any moment she will walk through a door in my home and be there. I am now able to feel a desire to be with someone else, and it feels good. I believe for myself that I have accepted the loss and have now been able to adjust and go on.

I found the next three concepts in a handout several years ago, and I do not know who to give credit to, but I know they are very real.

3 Kinds of Grief

1) Immediate

This is when our reaction to a loss occurs at the time of the loss, or prior to if we are aware of the impending difficulty.

2) Delayed

This is when someone seemingly has little or no reaction to the loss. It may appear to others that this person is being strong and a "pillar of strength." Others admire how well this person has handled the situation and may lean on them for support. Later on, when the person finally starts to feel the reality of what has happened (often times when everyone is gone and he or she has time alone), the griever can have a variety of reactions involving any or many of the seven stages. People are surprised when this person reacts, falls apart, or just becomes unable to cope with life, because he or she was so strong during the initial loss. Anyone who does this will have to navigate through at least some stages of grief and deal with it sometime.

3) Minimal Reaction

Due to a profound religious or philosophical belief, some may have minimal reaction to loss. This is self-explanatory and some people handle loss much better than the average population because of such beliefs.

It is important to discuss these stages with those involved as soon as possible; it is also appropriate so they know what to expect. This information helps them to realize that they are going through a natural healing process which takes time.

The Social Adjustment Scale

This is a scale devised by Thomas H. Holmes and Richard H. Rahe, M.D.'s. [4] They came up with a method of measuring how much stress certain losses in life cause. This is measured on a scale of 1 to 100. Some of these losses are listed here.

---

4   Holmes T.H., Rahe, R.H. (1967). "The Social Readjustment Rating Scale". *Journal of Psychosomatic Research 11* (2): 213–8. doi:10.1016/0022-3999(67)90010-4.

Stress of Adjusting to Change

Events	Scale of Impact
Death of a spouse	100
Divorce	83
Marital separation	65
Jail term	63
Death of a close family member	53
Marriage	50
Fired at work	47
Marital reconciliation	45
Retirement	45
Change of health of family member	44
Pregnancy	40
Sex difficulties	39
Gain of new family member	39
Business readjustment	39
Change in financial state	38
Death of close friend	37
Change to different line of work	36
Change in number of arguments with spouse	35
Large mortgage	31
Foreclosure of mortgage or loan	30
Change in responsibilities at work	29
Son or daughter leaving home	29
Trouble with in-laws	29
Outstanding personal achievement	28
Wife begins or stops work	26
Begin or end school	26
Change in living conditions	25
Revision of personal habits	24
Trouble with boss	23
Change in work hours or conditions	20
Change in schools	19
Change in sleeping habits	17
Vacation	13
Christmas	12

Some Suggestions When Someone Dies

Depending on your circumstances, one of the best things you can do is contact a mortuary for step-by-step directions upon the death of a loved one. Most funeral homes have individuals who will help with lists of important tasks to complete at these times. If a preplanned funeral has been arranged, then you will be less stressed in a stressful time. If hospice is involved and the family member dies at home, they will declare the death and time and may assist with the transport of the body. This may be a simple call to the mortuary who will arrange to take the loved one to their facility.

Consumer Reports has a very nice checklist available online called, "What to do when a loved one dies. Our advice can keep a sad event from becoming even more painful." I found that the two mortuaries I used were very helpful in assisting me to complete all the tasks from the funeral arrangements to contacting Social Security and other necessary details when my wife died. I have compiled lists from various mortuaries' "lists of things to do." below:

- Obtain copies of Death Certificate; mortuaries usually obtain this for you (if there are many assets several copies will be necessary)

- Create an obituary (generally mortuaries will place the obituary in the paper and online)

- Create a program for the funeral if you plan on having one

- Obtain copies of the obituary because you will likely need this as proof of death for life insurance benefits and more

- Make copies of newspaper articles (regarding the deceased for proof of death)

- Obtain Certificates of Appointment from a court (if you are the executor, administrator or have any other financial responsibility for the deceased)

- Check the safe deposit box if one exists

- Talk to an attorney about filing a will or other documents

- Review any insurance policies and determine who the beneficiaries are as well as heirs

- If the deceased is a veteran, review any military records and check with your local veteran's affairs office to determine if they will provide a headstone and program at the funeral

- Apply for veteran's benefits, Social Security benefits, life insurance benefits, pension benefits

- Contact the human affairs division of the company where the deceased worked and inquire regarding any benefits he or she may have accrued

- Contact all creditors and inform them of the death

- Transfer all titles from home and vehicles to your name

- Contact the three credit reporting agencies and inform them of the death of the person. This is necessary because you don't want someone to steal the identity of the deceased and begin causing financial problems.

Experian   1-800-397-3742   www.experian.com
P.O. Box 2002
Allen, TX 75013

TransUnion   1-800-916-8800   www.transunion.com
P.O. Box 1000
Chester, PA 19022

Equifax   1-800-685-1111   www.equifax.com
P.O. Box 740241
Atlanta, GA 30374

This is not a complete list of things to do when a loved one dies but it will give you a good start. Your funeral home and attorney will be able to help you with other tasks that may be necessary in your area depending on local laws.

chapter seven

POSTTRAUMATIC STRESS DISORDER

This is a condition which is caused by traumatic events such as war, torture, physical assaults, sexual abuse, witnessing death, serious accidents, disasters of all kinds, or anything that threatens the well-being of a person. This is a simple definition of what is referred to as PTSD. We have all heard of veterans who have come back from battle who have been horribly affected by their experiences. I have seen many victims of sexual abuse, domestic violence, terrible accidents, and other tragedies with this diagnosis. You may also know people who have some symptoms of PTSD who experienced divorce or other difficult circumstances in life. I believe the time is overdue for the public to understand the description and symptoms of this disorder.

Caution!

Only licensed professionals are qualified to diagnose this disorder and all other disorders described in this book. I include the definition and symptoms for educational purposes. If you or someone you love has enough symptoms to cause you concern, you should make an appointment with a licensed professional for an assessment, leaving the diagnosis to him or her.

The diagnostic definition of this condition will help further demonstrate how devastating it is. This description is from the DSM-IV or

Diagnostic and Statistical Manual of Mental Disorders referred to in other areas of this book. PTSD is grouped in the DSM manuals under Anxiety Disorders, however I have placed it here in its own chapter because I believe it needs to be addressed on its own merits so that it doesn't get lost within the category of Anxiety Disorders. With a significant number of the population experiencing this disorder, it is critical that we all understand it more fully. In order to receive permission to use this and other definitions of mental disorders, I was unable to put the definition of PTSD in simpler terms. I hope the technical language is not too confusing.

Posttraumatic Stress Disorder

A) The person has been exposed to a traumatic event in which both of the following were present:

- the person experienced, witnessed, or was confronted with an event or events that involved actual or threatened death or serious injury, or a threat to the physical integrity of self or others

- the person's response involved intense fear, helplessness or horror. Note: In children, this may be expressed instead by disorganized or agitated behavior

B) The traumatic event is repeatedly reexperienced in one (or more) of the following ways:

- recurrent and intrusive distressing memories of the event, including images, thoughts, or perceptions. Note: In young children, repetitive play may occur in which themes or aspects of the trauma are expressed.

- recurrent distressing dreams of the event. Note: In children, there may be frightening dreams without recognizable content.

- acting or feeling as if the traumatic event were recurring (includes a sense of reliving the experience, illusions, hallucinations, and dissociative flashback episodes, including those that occur on awakening or when intoxicated). Note: In young children, trauma-specific reenactment may occur.

- intense psychological distress at exposure to exposure to internal cues that symbolize or resemble an aspect of the traumatic event

- physiological reactivity on exposure to internal or external cues that symbolize or resemble an aspect of the traumatic event

C) Persistent avoidance of stimuli associated with the trauma and numbing of general responsiveness (not present before the trauma), as indicated by three or more of the following:

- efforts to avoid thoughts, feelings, or conversations associated with the trauma

- efforts to avoid activities, places, or people that arouse recollections of the trauma

- inability to recall an important aspect of the trauma

- markedly diminished interest or participation in significant activities

- feeling of being detachment or estrangement from others

- restricted range of affect (e.g., unable to have loving feelings)

- sense of a foreshortened future (e.g., does not expect to have a career, marriage, children, or a normal lifespan)

D) Persistent symptoms of increased arousal (not present before the trauma), as indicated by two (or more) of the following:

- difficulty falling asleep or staying asleep

- irritability or outbursts of anger

- difficulty concentrating

- hypervigilance

- exaggerated startle response

• Duration of the disturbance (symptoms in Criteria B, C and D have been ongoing for more than 1 month.

• The disturbance causes clinically significant distress or impairment in social, occupational, or other important areas of functioning.

The symptoms are described as acute if they have been ongoing for less than three months or chronic if they have been experienced for more than three months. They are considered as delayed onset if the symptoms start six months or more after the trauma.[5]

If you or anyone you know shows signs of this disorder, please do all you can to obtain professional help. It is unlikely that anyone with this problem will resolve it on their own or with simple support from friends and family without intervention by mental health professionals. Treatment may require both therapy and medication. The military is stepping up efforts to assist veterans in dealing with this terrible problem experienced by many who have experienced the battle field. Some of the methods used in treatment are described in the chapter entitled, ANXIETY DISORDERS.

---

5   American Psychiatric Assiciation. (1994). *Desk Reference to the Diagnostic Criteria from DSM IV,* pp. 209-211. ISBN: 0-89042-064-5

chapter eight
VICTIMS OF SEXUAL ABUSE

Sexual abuse has been something I have treated since I started practicing over 35 years ago. In my first year of meeting with clients, I was shocked to discover that about 50% of the women I met with revealed they had been abused sexually sometime in their life. Most commonly, these women came to see me because of depression. When we got to the real cause of their depression, sexual abuse was the underlying reason. From that point on I have asked all my clients if they have ever been touched or sexually abused.

As I became more concerned about this epidemic of victims I was seeing, so were other clinicians. The time frame was the early 1980s, and there arose a ground swell of awareness and focus on these individuals. Treating victims and protecting young children from abuse was the theme of many professional conferences and law enforcement efforts. Changes in laws requiring clergy to report abuse resulted in much more protection for abuse victims and greater public awareness of this problem. We have much further to go regarding abuse prevention, but this period in time to which I am referring was the real beginning of a positive change in how abuse is dealt with today.

Because I have much therapy experience with victims of sexual abuse, most of what I discuss in this chapter will apply to these individuals. There are many similarities in therapies for sexual abuse which apply to victims of physical and emotional abuse. In book 3 of this series, I have addressed DOMESTIC ABUSE AND WOMEN'S SHELTERS in the chapter of the same name, which can include sexual, physical and emotional abuse. If you know of anyone who is being abused in any way, I encourage you to contact the resources described in that chapter. Local women's shelters and hotlines for abuse can be found in most cities across the country. You can receive help and protection if you reach out to these organizations created for victims of many forms of abuse.

Adults Molested As Children or AMAC

As I counseled with many victims of sexual abuse and learned more about their struggles I began to develop a strong bond with them. I wanted to help them in every possible way, so I went to as many training opportunities as possible. An acronym was created to describe these victims called AMAC or Adults Molested as Children. This description includes those who have become victims from infancy to young adulthood.

What is Sexual Abuse

Sexual abuse is any coerced or forced sexually stimulating behavior between a child and an adult or another child who is in a position of power, trust, or control. The abuser who is usually older uses manipulation and or threats to force the victim to cooperate and not tell others. In most cases the victim knows the abuser. The abuser can be a parent, step-parent, sibling, extended family member, acquaintance, baby sitter or stranger. When an abuser is trusted, is older, or is in a position of power over the victim, it is extremely difficult for the victim to stop the abuse. Think of how often children are told to obey adults and then consider how young victims are vulnerable to pressure from an older offender to do what he or she wants.

The Abusers

Abusers come from every kind of background from race to religion, occupation and income level, regardless of their education or status in society. Abuse occurs more often in homes where other problems exist, but it can also happen where there are no obvious indications of abuse.

How Victims React to Abuse

The threats used to keep the victim quiet are very frightening and therefore thoughts of reporting the abuse are out of the question. The victim literally believes he or she has no way to stop the abuse because the abuser is older, stronger, and knows how to control his or her victim. This is what sets up the victim to continue being a victim, in many cases, until he or she leaves home or the offender moves or any other number of reasons including the abuse becomes known to others and is reported. This powerless feeling of being unable to say, "No," stays with victims, sometimes for their entire lives.

In book number 3, in the chapter entitled HOW WE DEVELOP OUR INDIVIDUAL IDIOSYNCRASIES AND FEARS, there is a statement from the book, Frogs into Princes that describes how we learn fears. Essentially, when we are under great stress sometime earlier in our lives, we make a decision regarding what we believe about ourselves, and every time a similar situation occurs, we react the same way. We believe and do the same thing in response to that situation. It might be that someone is bitten by a dog and the fear of dogs remains for life. A child is bullied and becomes a recluse. Someone's heart is broken and he will no longer trust in love. A child or young adult is sexually abused and may be threatened that if he or she tells, he or she will be in trouble or even that the abuser will kill his or her family. When a child is told this by an adult or older child, he or she believes it, but the child cannot understand why that would be so. Because the victim knows that the offender is stronger, smarter, and is in control, the child believes what he or she is told. Without the possibility of escape, the belief in being unable to escape any similar situation is developed and strengthened after each successive episode of abuse. You can see how in other situations like dating, if a female is being pressured into sexual activity that the victim does not have the ability to say no, because she had no power to stop the abuse earlier in life. It is as if the victim is experiencing the previous abuse all over again. They feel the same helplessness and horror present during the initial abuse. Essentially, they become a child again, unable to stop the abuse. The same belief continues on, sometimes for a lifetime, unless he or she gets help. Victims can develop Posttraumatic Stress Disorder, wherein they have flashbacks of former abuse and anything similar to that abuse causes overwhelming feelings of despair and often the inability to do anything about it. To understand this more fully it would be well to read the chapter on POSTTRAUMATIC STRESS DISORDER.

Victims of Spouse Abuse or Rape

Victims of spouse abuse or rape can experience long-term damage similar to child abuse victims. It is important for these victims to get professional help and protection from the abuser. The information in the chapter on Domestic Violence can be helpful in these situations. Rape crisis phone numbers in your local area are found with a simple search on the web or by phone. The National Sexual Assault Hotline phone number is 1-800-656-HOPE (4673). This is a national organization and network of trained volunteers called RAINN or Rape, Abuse & Incest National Network. When a call is made to this number a computer notes the area code and sends the call to the nearest RAINN center. This is a safe, anonymous, and confidential call and the caller's phone number is not retained unless the caller chooses to share personal identifying information. They also have a very helpful website: www.rainn.org. You will find information there on reporting, helping a loved one, finding a local counselor, state resources, communicating with law enforcement, and much more.

Manipulation of the Victim by the Abuser

Offenders are very good at manipulating victims so they will not talk. Let's look at some of their methods. They tell their victims that it is their fault and that they really want to do bad things. They also tell them that they are not good for anything but sex and that they are worthless, especially if others find out about it. If others know about it, then they will know how dirty and disgusting they really are. As mentioned above, they tell the victims they will kill them or their family. I have heard victims report that their fathers told them that teaching them how to have sex is something that fathers are supposed to do to prepare them for marriage. There are no depths that an offender will not go to in order to manipulate and make sure the victim won't talk. This is why many victims do not make their abuse known until they are older adults and, in some cases, victims may never tell. There are many other twisted reasons offenders use to coerce victims including the lie that they are showing their love for them.

Guilt Magnified by the Physiological Response to Stimulation

The human body is designed to feel pleasure when stimulated sexually. When the sexual time clock is started early for a young child by sexual abuse, the feelings of sexual arousal can be triggered and a victim can feel pleasure. These victims feel conflict between being used by the offender and the pleasurable feelings they experience. They have an innate sense that what they are being forced into doing is not good or right. They may also feel a counterfeit form of caring and closeness that they may have never experienced in their family. They might not have been told they were loved or may not have been embraced by their parents, thus reinforcing the counterfeit love and attention they receive from the abuser. If the offender manipulates by telling the victims that they are doing this because of love, it becomes more confusing and a young victim cannot see the real truth that he or she is being abused. In some cases, because the abuse is so frequent, it is not uncommon for the child over time to initiate the sexual actions he or she has been taught by the abuser. Because it becomes pleasurable it may be the only time the child feels loved. Victims can believe that the only thing they are good for is sex, and they seek comfort in sexual behavior. I have seen so many sad situations where a young person has become so convinced he or she is unworthy to be loved that they gravitate to drugs, alcohol, and other people who also believe this about themselves. It can become very difficult to help these individuals change their belief system when it becomes deeply engrained.

When victims become old enough to understand that sexual behavior at such an early age is inappropriate, they frequently feel guilty and worthless. They wonder why they were abused and believe that something is wrong with them to have caused the abuse. A much deeper sense of shame and guilt can develop if the victim enjoyed and at times instigated the behavior, after the abuser hooked him or her in. You can see how many of these victims become so distraught that they turn to self-defeating behaviors.

Behaviors Common to Victims of Abuse

Long-term emotional damage results from abuse including guilt, fear, self-hatred, low self-esteem, alienation from family and caring friends, depression, being overly affectionate, seductive or other inappropriate behavior, rebelliousness, drug abuse, promiscuity, vulgar language and behavior, preoccupation with sex in language and behavior, running away, attempts of suicide, withdrawal, and lack of trust for adults. They may only desire to associate with the wrong crowd who are into drugs, alcohol, sex, and extreme alternate lifestyles, much different from how they were raised. Dress and grooming may become extreme. Others can develop eating disorders such as bulimia or anorexia nervosa. It is estimated that over 75% of those who have eating disorders have been sexually abused. Victims with eating disorders become perfectionistic and overly critical of their appearance, thinking that they are too fat. These individuals go overboard in an attempt to control their world by controlling their weight and how and what they eat. There are other details of eating disorders that I do not have time or space to address in this book. However, in the majority of eating disorder cases, the treatment and recovery can be very long and most frequently needs intense treatment options, including hospitalization in some cases. For sure, individual and group therapy with help from dieticians are the basic elements in treating these individuals. This is a highly specialized type of treatment and experts who are trained in this field should be sought for someone dealing with eating disorders. An internet web search for "eating disorders treatment," should reveal someone in your area. They may also be found in local phone books or the yellow pages online.

Some victims gain weight because they believe they will not be attractive to those who might want to use them sexually. You can imagine how they can beat themselves up mentally and feel absolutely worthless to the point that they may never date or marry. This can lead to a life of loneliness and desperation.

Some intelligent people have observed that it is important to not minimize the impact of any type of abuse because a child exposed to mild abuse may be as injured emotionally as one exposed to severe abuse. If abused children are not helped they may develop bitterness toward life, themselves, and others. When they are older they may be unhappy or struggle in marriage, and they may even abuse or neglect their own children. I have had some clients over the years with excessive fears that they will abuse their children. Just because someone has been abused does not mean they will abuse their children or others. If someone is concerned about this, it is less likely that he or she will do so. If you are worried about this issue, I recommend you get some professional help.

When Parents Do Not Protect Their Children

There are very sad situations which I have seen all too often in sexual abuse cases. This is when a mother ignores the sexual abuse her husband inflicts on a daughter or son because she dislikes sex altogether. Often this happens because the mother was sexually abused herself, resulting in no desire to be involved sexually with her husband. When this is true, the mother will have the same symptoms discussed in this chapter. Any kind of exposure to the chance of sexual behavior can cause extreme anxiety and even fear. Therefore, if the situation arises where the father or stepfather begins to abuse daughters or sons, the mother may turn a blind eye to it. In some cases, mothers can even encourage this behavior by being out of the home at opportune times when the husband and children are there together. There can be many more ways the mother sets up or just ignores the abuse, even when a daughter or son tells her about it.

This sounds strange that a mother, who had sex with her husband or a partner to have children earlier in life, would have problems later in life with sexual intimacy. This fact helps us to understand how devastating sexual abuse is to an individual and how it often affects a victim for a lifetime. These victims will just put up with sex in order to have children and keep the marriage from ending in divorce. Many marry and continue to feel like a victim of sexual abuse in their marriage because their feelings about sexual contact are the same as they were when they were abused. They may take these feelings and fears of intimacy with them into adulthood, marriage, and beyond unless they get professional help and finally heal. In essence, both they and their children stay victims and become victims.

You can imagine how this would affect a child who is not protected by his or her mother. The abuse endured by the child is bad enough, but when it becomes evident that the mother was, in fact, not protecting him or her, the results can be very devastating to the child. This can cause lifelong problems with self-esteem, anger, worthlessness, and much more. Obviously, the relationship between the victims and their mothers are difficult, to say the least. Some of these mothers feel tremendous guilt and others have been so traumatized by their own abuse that they do not have the capacity or desire to recognize what they have done. I have seen many cases where the mother denies knowing the abuse was taking place and the victim or victims know she is lying because the facts do not support her claim. The child victim may harbor diverse feelings of resentment and other emotions toward their mothers all their lives. This is a very complex and insidious problem that victims need to deal with when they are ready. In most cases, it is best if this happens before the parent or parents are no longer living, if that is possible for the victim to do. This can also extend to both parents if the victim believes they ignored the abuse by another offender, either inside or outside the family.

The Path to Security, Love and Self-Esteem

I developed this handout many years ago to demonstrate, in a very simple way how we develop security, love and self-esteem, and how this process can be interrupted and even destroyed by sexual abuse. I have found that abuse victims relate to these descriptions and it helps them see what has happened to them in terms of corrupting their security, self-love, and self-esteem.

SECURITY, LOVE AND SELF-ESTEEM

AGE	NEEDS	SOURCE
Infant	Love, Cuddling, Nurturing	Mother, Father and Family
Child	Love, "I love you", Cuddling	Mother, Father and Family
Teen	Love, Acceptance, Belonging	Peers and Family
Adult	Love, Intimacy	Husband or Wife

When this process occurs naturally then normal social development follows. You will note that intimacy is meant to take place in the last stage as an adult. However, when intimacy is introduced too early during the child or teen stages, the victim takes guilt, lack of trust, and many other symptoms discussed above into adulthood with him or her. The results can be devastating and lifelong if not treated and resolved.

Choosing a Therapist

It is important to choose a therapist that you feel comfortable with and at the same time knows what he or she is doing. This is a very sensitive and critical responsibility for a therapist. A victim may take years to gain the strength to seek counseling. It is important to go to someone who is trained and or experienced in sexual abuse treatment. You or your child may have strong feelings about going to a male or female counselor so make a choice about that issue and pursue that course until you find someone who appears to fit the bill. Contacting RAINN or Rape, Abuse & Incest National Network mentioned previously, is a great place to help find a treatment center. You can also search online for sexual abuse treatment in your local area. Check with your insurance provider by calling the mental health phone number on the back side of your insurance card to make sure they will cover your therapy. They may even have a list of providers they allow you to go to.

Individual Therapy and Group Therapy

My experience as a therapist with victims of sexual abuse led me to take them through a twofold process. The first step was to get the patient either completely through his or her individual therapy or far enough along that I believed he or she was ready to go into group therapy. The second step, was group therapy. Group therapy can be very beneficial for each patient to experience because there are many things to be gained from knowing, interacting with, and building relationships with other victims. When a person is ready, group therapy accelerates the process of healing, not only for him or her but for everyone in the group. When a victim knows that he or she is not alone and that others have gone through similar experiences, the bonding that takes place gives these victims greater hope and confidence, as well as many other positives.

It is important for a victim to not be involved in group therapy prior to individual therapy. This is not wise because there needs to be a great deal of step-by-step progress before a victim can benefit from the group experience. I had the unfortunate experience of allowing someone into one of my groups before she had any individual therapy, and it was not a good result. I was traveling out to a city twice a month doing therapy with several victims of sexual abuse and eventually it came time to start a group with these individuals. We had finished our second group therapy session and soon after I received a call from an ecclesiastical leader who asked me to include a woman in the group. He had referred several women to me and had heard how helpful the group was for them. He almost insisted that I included her. She had been abused by her father and had just become aware that he had abused her sisters also. These sisters were all adults with families of their own and they met together for a family gathering. When they were alone together one of them brought up the subject, opening the flood gates, and they all revealed they had been abused by their father. They confronted him and he denied everything. The pain, resentment, anger and confusion these sisters felt was enormous. Together they went to the prosecuting attorney of the county where he was a prominent member of the community. This started a long process that eventually resulted in a prison sentence. I have seen this same scenario happen more than once.

I met with this woman once and then reluctantly allowed her to attend our next group session. I don't recall the subject of the group discussion that evening but it set her off and she became angry and left. The fact is that the other members of the group had dealt with their abuse in individual therapy, and they were much farther along in their progress, and they were ready to deal with the issues they faced in the group. Because they were openly discussing and processing their abuse it seemed to this woman that they were minimizing what they all had experienced. I attempted to contact her but she would not respond. I hope she and her sisters received proper treatment. I spoke to her husband and explained that I should not have allowed her to come to group therapy without individual therapy first. He understood and he was a very supportive and caring spouse. My point here is that I believe every victim of sexual abuse needs to complete individual and where possible group therapy. I know that in some rural areas this may be difficult, and I hope every victim can eventually have that experience. It would be well to recognize here that many victims are highly reluctant or intimidated by the idea of group therapy. Each person is unique and should not be pushed. This is why the workbook

I refer to later in this chapter is important to help victims deal with their issues in a more private and personal manner. There has been a general tendency during the last several years, to not emphasize the group experience as it once was.

I make these statements with some feelings of guilt because I only do therapy on a part time basis now, and I don't have enough AMAC patients at anyone time to form a group. Because of this I make sure my patients who have eating disorders are referred to an appropriate therapist who not only treats this additional issue but also provides a group treatment experience. I also make sure my patients are firmly grounded and that we have dealt with all the specific topics discussed here later and that every concern expressed by the patient is addressed prior to completing therapy. This is not ignoring the fact that the patient may well need to return at any point in time for additional follow up.

You can imagine how victims of sexual abuse might respond to everyday experiences that remind them of their abuse, including news and any references to sexual behavior and abuse or other situations that trigger feelings of helplessness and the inability to control what happens to them. This can cause victims to react in ways that are dysfunctional and cause problems in the work place, marriage, family and social life, as with the example described above. In other words, many of the problems we see in lives of individuals, marriages, etc. may have their genesis or start in sexual abuse.

Victims Have No Guilt

There is a statement on this subject from people who really understand this subject that I read to all my clients. I am going to paraphrase what it says here. I do this because almost every victim feels deep, unnecessary guilt. Understanding and reinforcing the following key point with a victim is critical in sexual abuse treatment.

Paraphrasing, victims of rape or sexual abuse frequently experience serious trauma and unnecessary feelings of guilt. Therapists and anyone involved should handle such cases with sensitivity and concern, reassuring such victims that they, as victims of the evil, immoral, and illegal acts of others, are not guilty of any wrong doing, helping them to overcome feelings of guilt and to regain their self-esteem and their confidence in personal relationships.

Young victims of sexual abuse are likewise not guilty of wrong doing where they are too young to be accountable for evaluating the significance of sexual behavior. Even where acts are committed with the apparent consent of a young person, that consent may be ignored or qualified for the purposes of moral responsibility where the aggressor occupied a position of authority or power over the young victim.

Guilt and Responsibility in Older Victims

Many victims believe they don't have the ability to say no, even when they are adults. This is because every time they are faced with a situation similar to the original abuse, where they had no power to say no, they feel like they are back in the exact same situation where they were forced into complying with the abuser. They literally feel like a helpless child and thus we have the effects of a posttraumatic stress disorder circumstance, including the flashbacks of sights, sounds, and feelings of the original, terrible abuse. Many of these victims become numb and do not respond, but simply go along as they had to in the beginning. They may react in many different ways, but they feel helpless and unable to do anything to stop these unwanted advances. I believe adult victims stay victims and are blameless for their behavior, until they can finally comprehend that they have the ability to stop the abuse and believe they don't have to be used any more. Don't believe you are guilty or bad if you cannot say no or even if you seek sexual behavior for comfort. Do you hear me? I maintain victims are not accountable for their behavior in these circumstances until they no longer feel like a defenseless child. This is true because they are still experiencing posttraumatic stress.

It is very gratifying to see clients who reach a place of strength, where they believe they can say no. For many this is the beginning of a new life, free from bondage and guilt and full of empowerment.

When this happens and you get the help you need, you will be starting your life over again and you can create the life you desire. You can do this!

Posttraumatic Stress Disorder and Dating

You can imagine how difficult it is for a victim of sexual abuse to begin the dating process. There are those who fall victim to abusers and believe they only deserve to be with abusers despite how difficult it is to be used over and over again. Then you have those who look for love and affection through sex because they believe it is the only way they can be loved. There are those who struggle mightily because dating is like opening themselves up to the tremendous fear of being sexually abused by the opposite sex. This is especially true for women who do not trust men and believe, with good reason, that all they want from a girl is sex. Each time they are with a male they fear they will be pressured into sex because they are not strong enough to say no. As mentioned previously and in each of these situations I have described, they feel as if they are a child again and have no way out. This is a horrifying feeling for them. There are many other scenarios I could describe but these are the most common ones with the patients I see in my practice. Of course, there are similarities with male victims of sexual abuse as they enter the teenage years.

Physical and Emotional Abuse

For children who are abused physically and emotionally, watch for unexplained bruises, welts, burns, fractures, lacerations, or abrasions, especially to the face. Children may be wary or anxious around adults or may be withdrawn, aggressive, frightened of a parent or parents, or fearful when other children cry.

What Can We Do When We Think Abuse Has Taken Place?

The first thing we can and should do is to believe the victim and make sure a call is made to the proper authorities. Child Protective

Services is a common name for agencies that protect children. They may be called by other names in different communities and they are located in every area of the U.S. and Canada. If you cannot find a local number then call RAINN, referred to in this chapter, and they will assist you. These calls are confidential and your name will not be made known. Secondly, reassure the victim that he or she is not to blame for the acts of the abusers. Because abusers use manipulative guilt to keep the victim from talking, it is important to recognize that the victim will blame him or herself for the abuse. Often younger children withdraw and do not want to talk. Adolescents may demonstrate distrust, resentment, anger, hatred, etc. You can be sure he or she feels guilt albeit false guilt, generated by the abuser. Help them let go of this damaging belief. If the abuser is a member of the family, be very careful to not condemn the abuser. Victims may still love the offender and criticizing can cause more harm than good. This sounds confusing to others, but it is often true. The dynamics of abuse within a family are very complicated and seem to defy logic at times. Do all you can to help keep the victim away from the abuser. In almost every case the abuser should be the one to leave the home. In the past it was common to remove the victims from the home to place them in foster care, which validated to the victims that they were the guilty ones. In most contemporary cases the perpetrator is the one who is arrested and removed from the home. Unfortunately, in some cases, the abuser is so manipulative and threatening that the other parent and children are afraid to report or support the victims when interviewed by the authorities. These are very difficult situations, and it can be complex for the truth to be revealed.

The Abusers

As mentioned the abusers, offenders or perpetrators as they are called, come from every economic level, race, religion, and background. When confronted they deny any wrong doing and are excellent at lying. I used to work with offenders but found that they are generally dishonest in therapy and will say anything the therapist wants to hear in order to escape any responsibility. This is why it is better to allow the court system to require treatment so it is ordered and enforced. Even so, it is widely accepted that pedophiles are very difficult to rehabilitate. There have been and always will be exceptions to this statement, but I believe that those who stop abusing are very small in number. Think of it this way, the most abhorrent crime after murder is child sexual abuse because it is child abuse of the worst form. It is viewed by society with such disdain that few offenders will admit to it. When the evidence is overwhelming they will comply, to a degree, but they cooperate only to receive the least possible consequences.

These individuals have learned to distort, lie, and hide their horrible acts and they become very good at it. They are terribly manipulative, and I simply don't trust them. I know that everyone needs a second chance; however, I believe we need to be very careful with these individuals. They can never be in a situation where they are alone with potential victims ever again. No matter how much therapy they have been in or the amount of time they have not perpetrated, they cannot be trusted concerning these matters.

Apologies from Abusers, Hardly!

Many victims of sexual abuse long for the offender to apologize to them. In my experience, this is something that happens rarely. Victims would feel better about themselves and respond more readily to therapy if they received an apology from the abuser. The guilt that comes with being a sexual abuse victim is so heavy that it prevents a victim from letting go of responsibility for the abuse. Victims have been so thoroughly brain washed by the offenders in order to keep them quiet that they believe they are the reason for the abuse. To receive an apology from the abuser would go a long way in helping the victim begin to realize that the offender was the one who manipulated them and used them sexually. What I am saying to victims here is never expect to receive an apology because it will probably not come, and if it does, it will be, in most instances, a half-hearted and unsatisfying manipulation. If an abuser does offer an apology, it is usually done as an assignment from the abuser's therapist, rather than a desire to tell the truth and ask for forgiveness. In the vast number of other cases where the abuse is not reported and the abuser is never brought to justice, victims should not expect an apology to come forth either. Victims cannot allow this fact to prevent them from healing as they receive therapy or go through the process of healing from their abuse.

Issues in Therapy

Getting It All Out

When victims enter into therapy, they can be feeling anything from overwhelming anger to desperate depression and suicidal thoughts. I listen and attempt to establish a relationship, hopefully with some trust in me and what we will be doing. I tell victims that I have been doing therapy with AMACs for many years and that I have a deep commitment and desire to help them through the process of healing. I tell them that because of my experience I know exactly what we need to do, and I will show them step-by-step and hope they can learn to trust me. I also say that I hope they can consider my office as their safety zone, where they can say anything they want, scream, cry, or whatever and it is all okay. The only thing they can't do is hit me or throw things at me. I really say this but jokingly.

It is important to give them the permission to let go of all their feelings and say everything they have ever wanted to say about their abuse. To accomplish this, the first thing I ask them to do is to begin writing an open letter to their abuser/abusers and to tell them exactly how they feel. What I mean by an open letter is that they will be adding to this letter over time until they have said all they want to say to the abuser/abusers. It is not uncommon for victims to write more even after they have finished therapy. If they find they have more feelings they want to express, that is perfectly okay and not unexpected. When victims start to write, it does not matter how bad it sounds, it has to come out. This is when I give them the handout, "The Healing Process" in the chapter by the same name. The point being that the subconscious has a lot of memories and feelings stored away that need to be purged, like letting the steam out of a pressure cooker before it explodes. If someone feels furious and outraged about how he or she has been treated and says, "I am a bit upset about what you did to me," the rage and deep anger are still inside the subconscious waiting to get out. Victims must say how they feel with the same intensity they feel inside in order to really purge and get out those truly, honest feelings. This is done by writing a letter, over time, which we do not send, unless at the end of therapy the victim wants to send it or a form of it to the abuser/abusers. This process usually takes a lot of time with a pen and paper or at a computer. This can be done as a separate letter to each abuser or family member, such as a parent who has not protected the victim. It can be one long narrative that goes on and on and can jump from addressing one person to another because whatever comes out, comes out. It is important to go where the energy is and let all those feelings flow out through the pen or keyboard.

When I discuss this with new clients they often think they are supposed to send the letter to the abuser or whoever they are writing to. This is not the case; it is written only to let out all the hurt and pain. I always tell clients, when you are finished writing you will know, and with it will come a tremendous sense of relief. When the client gets to this point an amazing transformation occurs. The bitterness and pain felt toward the abusers and any others is replaced with pity and a type of calmness, peace, strength, and resolve. I tell them when they are through doing this they will know what they need to do with the letter/s. They can send the entire letter to the abuser, write a shorter version and send it, make a phone call, confront the abuser in person, tear it all up, burn it, just let it go, or anything they choose to do. I find it fascinating that very often, at the end of this process victims experience feelings of pity for the abusers. When this happens, they are able to let it go and get on with their lives. They know in their hearts what they need to do. I love to be witness to this transformation. It is nothing less than a miracle.

Other Methods to Express Feelings

There are two other methods under one technique that I use to help victims express their feelings and emotions. This is called the empty chair technique, and it can be used two different ways: visually in the mind and verbally. I don't know who came up with this method, but I learned it in graduate school, and it is very useful in many kinds of therapy situations. I use these same methods described in the chapters on, THE HEALING PROCESS and DEPRESSION DEFINITION AND TREATMENT.

The first step is to teach the victim relaxation and what is called guided imagery. I tell patients I am going to take them through some exercises to teach some important skills that will be valuable to them for the rest of their lives. I tell them that in order to do this, their eyes will be closed for about 10 minutes. I ask if they are experiencing any feelings and to rate those feelings on a scale from zero to 10 in terms of severity, zero being relaxed and almost asleep and 10 being as bad as it can get. This can be a sensitive and difficult thing to do because a victim of sexual abuse usually has issues with trust, especially with a male therapist for female victims. After identifying any feelings and how strong they are on this scale, I start the relaxation process by having them tighten and then relax each group of muscles from the feet, legs, torso, etc. to the head and neck, one at a time. Then I teach them three or four more exercises until we get to deep breathing. When I believe they are sufficiently relaxed, I ask them to visualize a beautiful, safe, warm place and then to look around and memorize all the details they see and experience. I do this because I want clients to go back there often in their minds so they get very comfortable with this process and place. Then I have them visualize the person they want to be someday, who has conquered all of her or his challenges and have that person stand by their side to be a support. I give instructions to see a chair appear. This is a special chair because anyone they place in the chair is restrained and cannot talk or move or do anything except to hear and understand everything the client says to him or her. I then instruct to have one of the people they want to talk to appear in the chair and then give them permission to tell that person anything they have ever wanted to say. They can scream, hit, kick, or do anything to that person they want and do so as long as they desire. When this is complete I tell the client to make the chair disappear and to allow the other "you" to stand next to them and offer support, maybe in the form of a hug or even verbally. I give directions to breathe slowly and deeply, and when it appears the client is relaxed they can open their eyes. It is amazing what this does for victims when they are able to do this. Feelings that have been buried for years are set free, and the anger dissipates each time this is repeated. I give them the assignment to go home and to continue doing this as often as possible. I also tell victims that every time they do this they will be able to identify how much anger and feelings they have let go on a scale of 0 to 100%.

There is another method of the empty chair technique I teach, which has the client sit alone in a room or anywhere else where there is a chair. The idea is to pretend the person the client wants to talk to is in the chair and then let it all out. This can be done while driving a car and imagining the person is in the passenger seat. Just don't get distracted while doing so. I have many of my other clients who are not abuse victims and have things to get of their chests do the same. It can be very freeing to say what you want out loud. This process of expressing emotions can go on for some time depending on the victim. It might be something that needs to be done on and off for weeks or months. The great thing about doing this is that each time it is done, it reduces the control the offender has over the victim. In addition, it tends to diminish resentment and anger in that person. This is an amazing process to observe as victims become more empowered and confident.

I have worked with some victims who are not ready to write how they feel or face the memories that writing would awaken. That is okay. When a victim is finally prepared and is willing to take the step, the healing process can begin. There are those who think they will never go there because it is so threatening to them. I hope they can gain the strength to someday get the help they need to heal and overcome. I believe by showing victims how this is done, they will gain the hope that can lead them through the healing process, which is different for everyone. Doing so makes it possible to take control of one's life going forward by putting away the deep feelings where they belong, with the one who caused the personal injury. You can do this!

I had a very beautiful and competent woman, who is at the top of her game in her profession, come to me and revealed her abuse by her father. No one at her office would ever have guessed that she was so bruised and damaged underneath the surface. She was so confident and competent at her job. Eventually, an abusive marriage and difficulty with children caused her to seek professional help. When I introduced the concept of writing her feelings or expressing them in her mind or verbally, she emotionally froze in my office and it took some time to get her to a state where she could leave and drive herself home. In such cases I offer support but never push the issue, and I hope someday she will be able to deal with her issues and get through a successful therapy experience. She was able to write how she felt toward her husband, which was a huge milestone. She comes in on occasion and I help her to apply rational thinking to her circumstances, and she is good for a period of time. Someday I think she will be ready to go forward and put it away where it all belongs, in the lap of the abuser.

The Next Step

These steps are not necessarily in a particular order because each person may need to take them in different orders and at different paces. After the victim has been able to communicate what she or he wants to accomplish in therapy and is able to express deep seeded feelings, we start to get into describing many of the misconceptions victims have believed about themselves, the offenders, and others.

Some time ago I was impressed by a handout a colleague of mine developed regarding the issues victims experience and must process until they come to a place of resolution or healing. I have used this in therapy, and it has proved to be very helpful for victims to see their lives described in black and white, right in front of them. Just knowing that others feel and respond in the same ways is very insightful and therapeutic. The following handout, "THE CONFUSION PROCESS," is from Dennis D. Perkins who is a clinical social worker experienced in treating AMAC victims. For my purposes here, I have changed a few of his points.

THE CONFUSION PROCESS

SITUATION	INTERPRETATION	EMOTIONS	TYPICAL BEHAVIORS
SEXUAL ABUSE	From Child's Perspective Pathogenic (or erroneous beliefs)		
Boundaries violated	My needsd and desires must not matter I'm not important, I"m here to meet everyone else's needs Others' needs are more important than mine	Helplessness Powerlessness	Passive in relationships (unassertive) Continues victim role (feel used) Hypersensitive in relationships and sensitive to rejection Puts up barriers to keep people at a distance to protect self from rejection, betrayal and hurt a. Withdrawal b. Aggression c. Constantly seeks approval from others and yet often discounts positives
Lured or forced to do something they did not want or intend	I'm easily manipulated My needs and feelings don't matter Others are deceptive and manipulative I am powerless around others	Fear Insecurity Powerlessness	Similar behaviors as above
Betrayal of trust by perpetrator, non-offending parents, body/feelings	I can't trust myself Others cannot be trusted Men cannot be trusted My mother should know what is happening and protect me-Perhaps I can't depend on others to help me My body is bad because it felt good	Confusion Anger	Puts up barriers to keep people at a distance to avoid being hurt Demonstrates resentment toward non-offending parent and men in general Shows distrust of others and their motives
Perpetrator says or does things to put blame on victim. A child thinks egocentrically (I have a part in, or cause, everything that happens)	I must have caused this It must be my fault I am a bad person If I was good enough, this wouldn't have happened Bad things happen to bad people	Guilt Shame	Takes responsibility for everything and everybody Escapes "guilt" through drug or alcohol abuse, eating, etc. Very cautious about what they say or do for fear of being found out

Natural, normal need to be nurtured is exploited by another for sexual gratification	I can't be loved just for me I am only good for one thing I can only be loved for sex Sex is bad Men only want one thing Men are exploitive I am to meet everyone's needs and my needs don't matter Does all touching lead to sexual touching? Love is exploitive and can hurt and often leads to sex	Confusion Loneliness Fear Isolation Guilt	Promiscuity/masturbation - nurturing sought through sexual contact Difficulties in sexual relationship a. Sensitive body parts, reminder of abuse b. Fear of being exploited by husband c. Flashbacks and bad memories may be triggered d. May avoid intimacy in marriage Puts up barriers to keep people at a distance for fear of being exploited or abused again Gains weight to be unattractive to men Becomes resentful toward men
Want to tell but afraid of consequences. May have told but is not believed, punished or brushed off	I caused this to happen and if I tell, I'll get in trouble I am bad No one believes me Maybe I'm crazy My feelings and thoughts don't matter	Isolated Helplessness Powerlessness	Repress memory and feelings to block out the pain and hurt Repression finds expression through physical and emotional symptoms: a. Nightmares b. Depression c. Unexplained health problems d. Bedwetting, encopresis e. Disturbed appetite f. Disturbed sleeping patterns g. Anxiety
Spiritual Implications: a. Prayed and asked God to help "daddy" stop it, yet it continued b. Learning about morality, chastity, being clean and preparing for marriage causes more confusion, etc. c. Sometimes the message is conveyed that if we are good, things will go well for us. If bad things happen, then I must not be good d. Statements like "You can be forgiven," implies the victim did do something wrong	God must not love me because he put me in this family or because he didn't answer my prayers I'm not worthy or good I am bad because bad things are happening to me I can't even trust God Praying doesn't help I'm not chaste or morally clean 'll never be god enough to marry a good person and have children Orhers must think I'm "bad" too	Confusion Guilt Shame Hopelessness Anger	Have difficulty praying Become rebellious in regard to religion Become perfectionistic to prove to God and others that they are "good"

You can see how victims can feel and act the way they do after reading these statements. When I discuss these sensitive issues with victims, they are often surprised at how they relate to the content. They live with and battle them every day. This is where we identify their cognitive or thinking distortions and then we work to change them and reassign them to the abuser where they belong. All the guilt and feelings as well as collateral damage described above must be dumped back on the abuser who caused them. This is a difficult process, to learn how to rethink and restructure what victims have believed for much of their life time, but it can be done.

I go over each of the areas covered in the confusion process with the victims. We completely digest how they foster these beliefs, and as victims express their emotions and confront their distortions they become empowered and stronger. Recognizing each time they think their distorted thoughts and then correcting them with logic and reason is vital to recovery and healing. Somewhere during this stage in therapy I tell them that, "Chastity cannot be taken it has to be given. It is a choice when someone uses free will to make that decision for her or himself." They literally come out of the dark and let go of the past manipulations to see themselves as they really are, beautiful, innocent, and full of self-worth. This is a beautiful thing to observe, and I can't wait for each person to say to me, "I don't need to come back any more; I believe I will be alright." They love themselves and become the person they were meant to be. What a thrill to be a part of such a transformation! I love it!

I also use with most clients, "The Courage to Heal Workbook: A guide for Women and Men Survivors of Child Sexual Abuse," by Laura Davis. She also has books with the same basic title that are excellent sources for anyone dealing with these issues. As I meet with my clients I have them work at a chapter per week if they are able. Sometimes it can be difficult for them to face the topics discussed and then to fill in their answers in the workbook. Some of my clients have to skip certain chapters and go back when they are ready. Some may not finish all the chapters, and that is okay. Laura Davis' books are a great way to get through to healing, and I recommend them.

Abusers Cause Distorted Thinking in Their Victims

I see many victims who believe they are bad people because they feel guilty for everything that happens in their lives. This is because the abuser has made them feel that way. When a child is told by an adult that sexual abuse is his or her fault, it creates defects in the child's ability to think rationally. The child begins to believe that other problems in life are his or her fault also. A child who is being abused does not have the ability to say to the abuser, "You are forcing me into this behavior, and if this was reported you would go to prison. I am innocent regardless of how you try to make me feel guilty to keep me from talking." Sexual abuse is even more insidious because the abuser distorts the victim's ability to think positively about his or herself. Victims are literally brain washed into believing they are worthless and that they deserved and wanted to be sexual, regardless of how young they are. This creates a feeling that they cause everything bad that happens to them.

I had a client many years ago who drew a cartoon to express how she felt guilty for everything in her life after her sexual abuse. I have kept this over the years because it is so typical of the feelings of most victims. I wish I could recall her name to give her credit for this very insightful illustration.

Underneath a cold granite rock a scrubby little bug sat hiding from the rest of the world. A big grasshopper kicked the rock over. "Stupid bug!" he said. "It's your own fault!"

"What is?" said Bug.

"I don't know. But whatever it is — it's your fault." And the grasshopper bounded away.

"He's probably right." thought Bug. "It always is my fault. Somewhere on a distant planet a three-legged creature is flunking its algebra exam and somehow — it's probably my fault."

In their efforts to keep the victims from talking, abusers effectively sentence them to a life of despair. The damage can be catastrophic. However, when the abuse stops for any number of reasons and if victims get professional help and support, they can heal and put all this behind them. When this happens I tell my clients that they can have control over their abusers. They can press charges or sue for damages and have great power over them, if they choose to. I say this not because I am encouraging them to do this but because it gives them a feeling of confidence they really need during therapy. That being said, there can be another level of healing for victims when the abuser/s are prosecuted, giving them public validation that they were truly victims of the illegal acts of others and that they are not the ones who deserved or caused the abuse. If victims choose not to pursue this path of litigation or prosecution they can still let everything go, heal and live happy lives, free from the effects of abuse. I know this sounds impossible to many victims who read this, but it really is possible.

Final Thoughts

Every time I work with victims of sexual abuse I feel I am walking on sacred ground. This is probably the most gratifying work I do. I dedicate this chapter to the victims of sexual abuse, and I want them to know that they can change their life and put these terrible experiences behind them. If you are a victim, I sincerely hope you can find the courage to go to a therapist who is experienced in treating sexual abuse and there find peace.

I tell victims I believe there will be a time in this life or in the next when justice will be done. I believe all perpetrators will come to know and feel exactly what they caused their victims to experience if they do not sincerely ask for forgiveness and do all they can to rectify what they have done. Call it Karma or Godly justice or whatever you want. I believe this is true; there will be final justice! Don't let the abuser continue to control you many years after the abuse; get help and become the strong and beautiful person you really are.

chapter nine

PERSONALITY DISORDERS: LIVING AND DEALING WITH VERY DIFFICULT PEOPLE

This chapter is one of the most important in this book. I truly believe if you purchased this book and only read this chapter it would be worthwhile sometime in your life to understand the difficult people you will encounter. For many years I have tried to preach the gospel of personality disorders to my small world of clients and acquaintances. Many people have heard of them; however, they don't know what they are. I intend to change this. Everyone needs to understand the characteristics of the 13 types of these disorders I am including in this book. It will make the world a more tolerable and insightful place. By being aware of these people it will assist many others to make better sense of their world and avoid long years of frustration and sorrow.

Do You Know Someone with a Personality Disorder?

Are there people you try to avoid because they make you feel uncomfortable or downright miserable? Is there someone in your life who is extremely difficult to be around? They might be demanding, self-centered, selfish and they never take personal responsibility. All the while they are experts at making you and others feel guilty and responsible for their happiness because you are not doing enough to make their life better. These people rarely if ever say, "I'm sorry." If this describes what you are experiencing with anyone then please read on.

111

On the other hand, you may have a loved one in your life who struggles with many aspects of living and he or she never seems to get better. No matter how much you try or how much others try to help, he or she just never gets better. Some get worse over time and despite attempts to encourage them to see doctors or to get therapy, they continue to struggle with life, but not to an extent (for most) that they seek help. Spouses and family members who stick with these people are, in my estimation, "Saints." In order to survive, some spouses and family members have to make hard decisions because they find they cannot take it anymore. They have given all they possibly can and when they realize that the other person will never change, they have to make a decision whether to:

Stay in the relationship and continue to give love and support, with no hope of getting anything in return or of the person ever changing. These are the Saints.

Stay in the relationship, but live their life as best they can and try to find happiness for themselves. They learn how to keep some emotional distance between them and their loved one by becoming desensitized to their helpless state. Sometimes they can engage with the other person and at other times they have to ignore him or her. To some degree or other they become numb to the other person's attempt to pull them back in and make them responsible for their happiness. In this case they live parallel lives with little meaningful in-teraction. Hopefully, these people can find something in life that gives them meaning and joy. This might mean embracing religion, goals, or dreams which have been placed on hold or finding new personal interests to make their lives meaningful.

Divorce, if they are a spouse or if they are a family member or loved one, they decide to keep an appropriate distance emotionally, physically, or both. If they live close by, they have to set hard rules and boundaries to stay away and have minimal or no contact. Sometimes they even have to move away to a safer distance to avoid being pulled back into the trap again. In some of these situations they can maintain contact if they are strong enough to not become entangled in the traps set for them. This works for some family members, but they need to be strong, not allowing the person with the personality disorder to control them.

Personality Disorders

If you are feeling controlled, manipulated, guilty, and always on the defensive and don't want to be around a certain person in your life, you may be dealing with someone who has a personality disorder. Some types of personality disorders are such that the person does not believe he or she has any problems. Such people do all they can to prove to the world that they should be treated differently than others because they are special. They never say I am sorry, and they are very good at manipulating others to do things for them. They can instill guilt in others with ease because they have been practicing this manipulative behavior for years. They are dictators in families, on jobs, and in relationships of all kinds. These are the people who take no thought of others because they are the most important people. You have seen these people in stores and social situations. They do not care if they keep a line of customers waiting behind them while they demand extra special treatment. How do you think the people who live with them feel?

In my first 12 years of practice, I saw so many of these Personality Disorders that I felt a responsibility to educate everyone about these very serious diagnoses. As I spoke to groups of people I handed out descriptions of these disorders to everyone who would listen. I found it to be a very satisfying experience to help people understand when they have others in their lives who have personality disorders.

There are 10 basic personality disorders with a few more additional ones. There have been books published about dealing with difficult people, and I hope I can give you further insight by understanding the underlying root of these behaviors, which in many cases is caused by a personality disorder. We all go through life knowing there are people who are hard to get along with, but we are left to our own devices to deal with them. I want everyone to understand what they are dealing with in relation to these hard to get along with folks, who in some cases dominate lives, families, and businesses with terrible consequences for all. Are you with me?

My First Exposure to Personality Disorders

When I was in graduate school, I was working at an agency two and a half days a week, completing what is called a practicum. I had a supervising therapist who was my practicum advisor, and I was assigned a few patients to work with. We were very fortunate because we had a consulting psychiatrist by the name of Dr. Christensen who came to our office twice a month and trained the staff. Dr. Christensen was a child prodigy and completed medical school at the age of 21. He was highly intelligent, down-to-earth, and he impressed me because, over the years as I ran into him, he always remembered my name and greeted me as if I was an old and good friend. He became director of the largest psychiatric hospital in the state.

As a student, I was included in this training and it was amazing. Each training session was conducted in the same fashion. Dr. Christensen would sit at the head of a very large table with the staff seated on both sides. He would review the file of a patient and go over the MMPI (the Minnesota Multiphasic Personality Inventory) a personality test that was administered to all of our clients. We would have a discussion of the client with the therapist who was seeing him or her and then the person would be escorted into the room and sat next to Dr. Christensen. He would then ask questions of the person, and when he was finished the patient would be excused. Dr. Christensen would then give us a diagnosis, and we would further discuss the prognosis (the likely outcome of treatment) and a treatment plan.

I remember very distinctly one of these training sessions. I can still see this attractive woman about 40 years of age with long dark hair, long coat and boots. I don't recall the questions asked or the responses of the client, but I do remember what happened when she left. Someone asked what the diagnosis was and Dr. Christensen said she had a personality disorder. The next question asked was, "What is the prognosis?" or what is going to be the probable outcome of her therapy. Dr. Christensen responded, "There is no prognosis; she has a personality disorder." He went on to explain that people with personality disorders don't change because they don't take personal responsibility for their behavior. That is the main component of their disorder; they don't take personal responsibility for their lives or their behavior. There is more, much more! He went on to explain that because they don't take responsibility for their behavior they don't believe they have any problems and therefore don't get help and don't change. I do not recall the specific personality disorder type she had. However, he was referring to personality disorders in general because those with personality disorders do not seek therapy because of the reasons described above. There are some types who take too much responsibility and suffer because of that belief. I will describe the various types and their symptoms.

Now back to the story. I was shocked and so were a few others there who had not seen such people in their practices. I could not accept the fact that this woman would not change because, as a naïve student, I believed everyone could change and that was why I wanted to be a therapist, to help them change.

The next question asked was, "If they won't change, what can we do to help these people?" He said, and I am paraphrasing here, all you can do is sit down with the family of the person and tell them that he or she has a personality disorder and he or she will not change. Therefore, they need to know this truth and then adjust as best they can or do what they have to do to survive in such a relationship. Indeed, in the realities of life some may have to divorce, reduce contact, or just ignore the person altogether, just to have some peace in life.

I walked out of that meeting in disbelief. I did not agree with what Dr. Christensen said, although I respected him very highly and knew he had more knowledge and experience than I did. Little did I know that I would become a believer by the end of my first year of practice.

My First Awareness of Someone in My Life Who Had a Personality Disorder

When I became aware of personality disorders I tried to understand my own family situation. I had a mother-in-law who, as I read the symptoms, it became clear that they fit her to a T. I talked to my wife about it, and we had to agree that it made complete sense and it really helped her understand her feelings about her mother. It was insightful and brought a lot of awareness to her relationship with her.

My wife loved her mother but she had a lot of deep-seated resentments toward her. Her mother was always right, and she ruled the home. I vividly recall her at Thanksgiving, standing in the middle of the kitchen in her apron with her hands on her hips ordering my wife and her sister around the kitchen. They did the vast majority of the work, but she took the credit for how hard she worked getting all the food prepared. My wife's self-esteem was greatly affected by her mother's strong and overshadowing personality. She always needed to be the center of attention and be in charge. If not, then lookout because she would go into high gear and get center stage if not by over-acting then by manufacturing an illness and going to the hospital or doctor. Over the years I was told that when her husband, a very good man, confronted her behavior early in their marriage her response was to get sick and she stayed in bed for six months. After this experience he never again took her to task by confronting her behavior again. After this experience I believe his methodology became somewhat passive aggressive toward her.

I liked my mother-in-law, but I did not have to live with her. I found myself avoiding certain subjects when around her and trying to keep everything on a light and happy positive level. At times she would want to talk to me alone about something very important, and I would find myself becoming very uncomfortable as she would tell me what was on her mind about my wife or psychology, etc. Her efforts were focused on convincing me that she was particularly smart and insightful, and I was not to tell anyone else what she was talking about. I avoided like the plague these secret meetings she wanted to have with me because it was so strange and, in my mind, over the top.

The best thing we ever did for my wife was to move to another state once I had finished graduate school. When this happened she began to find herself, and she blossomed into a competent and self-assured mother of seven children. She became the person I knew she could be when I first met her. That was the key for her, to get away from the constant overpowering exposure to her mother who had a good heart but in order to feel good about herself, she always made others, who allowed it, to feel like they had to please her. She could never quite match her mother's expectations. Little comments were always being sent out to remind her she didn't do this or that quite right. I don't believe she did this consciously because she did not have a mean bone in her body. She did this because she was so insecure within herself that her subconscious drove her constantly to be perfect and to expect perfection from others. When those around her were not performing to her standards, it was an indictment against her. In effect, her subconscious was telling her that she had to make sure her kids reflected her exacting standards and if they did not she would not hesitate to remind them. This came across as criticism and for a sensitive person it was quite difficult to not take personally. Curiously, she would brag about how wonderful my wife was to others but not when she was present. I loved my mother-in-law, and she was very fun at times, but everyone around her would have to admit that they had to tolerate her behavior.

Many Types of Personality Disordered People Do Not Seek Help

In my experience, this is true for Paranoid Personality Disorder, Antisocial Personality Disorder, Schizoid Personality Disorder, Histrionic Personality Disorder, Narcissistic Personality Disorder, Avoidant Personality Disorder, Obsessive-Compulsive Personality Disorder, and Passive Aggressive Personality Disorder. There are always exceptions to this statement; however, I have found this to be fairly consistent. These personality disorders are found in the DSM-IV or the Diagnostic and Statistical Manual for Mental Disorders published by the American Psychiatric Association.

The very description of a personality disorder precludes these individuals from making significant changes. Remember, they do not take responsibility for their behavior. The reason they don't is because they don't believe they have any problems and therefore why would they seek help? They blame others for their problems and believe if others would just do what they want them to that their lives would be better. They cannot ever admit that they have any problems. They are miserable to a degree but not enough to make any real changes or seek help. This would be too devastating to them. I believe they are so fragile in their psyche that they cannot, in any way, admit to any faults or say, "I am sorry". At times they may say something like, "I know I need to do this or that," but to say, "I'm sorry," is not in their vocabulary. That is another major aspect of this disorder. THEY NEVER SAY, "I'M SORRY." If on rare occasions they do, there is always a "but" that follows, placing blame back on someone else and effectively absolving them from responsibility.

The only time they come to see a therapist-counselor is when they accompany a spouse, child, or family member for one or possibly two sessions. They come in to demonstrate to the therapist that they are the sane one and that their spouse, child, or family member has the problem and not them. In effect they say, "Send my wife or child back when you have fixed them." You never see them again in most cases. They might come back to reinforce their case but not to make any changes themselves. Even if, by a miracle, someone wants help who has one of the above personality disorders, they don't last long. The first time they are confronted about their behavior even in the slightest way they are out of there.

Most of you know what I mean because you have been around someone in your life with whom you have to, "Walk on Eggshells". You probably did not know he or she most likely has a personality disorder!

LIGHT BULB! HELLO! DO YOU GET IT? THIS IS ONE OF THE MAJOR REASONS I WROTE THIS BOOK. THE GENERAL PUBLIC NEEDS TO KNOW ABOUT PERSONALITY DISORDERS.

Why Do You Suppose so Many People Get Divorced?

I know there are many reasons people get divorced, but there are a lot of people out there with personality disorders who are a major cause of divorce, and we all need to be aware of this reality. When they are dating, people with personality disorders do not show their real colors or their dark side until it is too late. This is the sad thing about these people; they can be very charming and impressive and are able to hide much of their dysfunction while dating. Usually, they start to show the real side, to some degree, just prior to marriage. It is sad when the unknowing partner senses something is not right but they push on thinking everything will be fine, because they are in love. What a shock when, after marriage, the real personality shows up. This is when the unsuspecting spouse says to himself or herself, "Who is this person? It certainly isn't the one I fell in love with." The control and guilt those with personality disorders spread to the other spouse is, in many cases, insidious. It can cause long-term, unspeakable damage to their spouse and children.

There are also cases when, over a longer period of time, one of the spouses can develop a personality disorder. This is called late onset and is less common than most people who develop them from the later teenage years to young adulthood.

Examples of Real Life Personality Disorders Which Caused Divorces

I have, unfortunately, had several female clients over the years that have had husbands who seem to be wonderful in every way to outside observers, but behind the scenes they are extremely controlling. An all too common example of this situation is when the husband has a good income and will only allow the wife to have very little money for her and the children to live off. This includes school lunches, clothes, gas for the car, etc. He expects her to take care of all the children's needs and hers and is totally indifferent and has no empathy, nor does he care when she requests more funds. He questions her on every item she purchases and wants to see the receipts. If she spends more on groceries than he thinks she should, she will be lectured and made to feel selfish and stupid. She is not allowed to have any extra to buy anything for herself or the children. In the particular case I am describing here (among many more of the same type), this husband bought himself whatever he wanted, and he was cold and calculating to his wife and children. He was detached from his family members and did not show emotion. He did not desire close relationships, including being part of a family. He almost always chose solitary activities. He had little interest in having sexual experiences with his wife. He did not seem to get pleasure from anything he did. He did not have close friends except for his parents. He was indifferent to praise or criticism, showed emotional detachment and little if any emotion.

As I have described this husband, I have outlined the criteria above for what is called Schizoid Personality Disorder, found later in this chapter. Eventually, his wife decided to divorce him because she came to understand that he would not change and she did not want to continue living like she had for more than 15 years. She loved being a stay-at-home mother and yet she became weary of feeling like a beggar. Essentially, she felt like a peasant woman with her peasant children. Sound familiar to anyone?

Another Example of a Different Type of Personality Disorder

I had this experience with a couple many years ago. They had several children and both husband and wife were sharp individuals. He was a very successful businessman, and she was a stay at home mother. One night, at the conclusion of playing basketball, the husband said, "Can I ask you a question?" I said, "Sure." He then asked me if I thought he was a good person. I was shocked, and I told him how surprised I was that he would ask such a question. I went on to tell him all the positives about him and the list was long. This seemed so strange that he would ask me this because he was so kind, personable, and professional. Later on, a situation arose in which this person did something out of character for him. He kissed another woman. This was absolutely inappropriate and caused real problems with everyone involved. His wife was understandably upset, angry, and humiliated. However, it became her crusade to destroy him. Yes, his behavior was unacceptable but the wife's reaction was a bit over the top, to those of us who were watching from the sidelines. She went to several people and wanted them to ostracize him personally and from their congregation. What she found was that most people were sympathetic to her situation but they did not want to punish and obliterate him as she did. Observers saw remorse in him and to tear him down did not seem like the answer in this circumstance.

What became very interesting is the fact that anyone who would not get on board with the wife and would not snub him and treat him with contempt, she cut off as well and would not associate with him or her anymore. She did this to several people. As time moved on, this couple divorced and the older children chose to live with their father. Later on, one of the younger children went to live with the father also. This was a shock to the supporters of the wife because they assumed the father was a terrible person. It was not surprising to those who knew the father.

I found out during their divorce that the wife's mother had deserted the family when she was a young girl. This made much more sense to me because the rejection she experienced from her mother was likely the reason she became so highly sensitized to the opinions of others. My theory is that her mother probably rejected her in many other ways before leaving the family, so it was probably a series of events causing her to feel unloved and probably unlovable. It is unknown in terms of all the specific reasons why people develop personality disorders, but it is clear that these kinds of life experiences, as expressed in this case, can be the reason for the onset of symptoms.

After observing the above situation, I reviewed the list of symptoms of Paranoid Personality Disorder. They had taken a personality test, and she scored high on the paranoid scale indicating she was highly sensitive to the opinions of others. She demonstrated a pervasive distrust and suspiciousness of others. She interpreted their motives as malevolent and suspected without real basis that others were exploiting, harming, or deceiving her. She believed she couldn't trust friends or associates and was reluctant to confide in others because of unwarranted fear that what she said would be used against her. She believed benign remarks were really demeaning or threatening, bore grudges, and was unforgiving of insults, injuries, or slights. She perceived attacks on her character or reputation that were not apparent to others and was quick to react angrily or to counterattack. She had recurrent suspicions, without justification, regarding the fidelity of a spouse or sexual partner. As I observed the events as they unfolded, I think this wife demonstrated all of these symptoms.

Personality Disorders: Who Are More Likely to Seek Help?

Individuals with the following personality disorders are more likely to seek help, but even so, they are in all likelihood not going to stay long in therapy and will probably not succeed in a remission of their symptoms. In my experience, this statement is true but there are always exceptions, although personality disorders are highly resistant to change. Schizotypal Personality Disorder, Borderline Personality Disorder, Dependent Personality Disorder, Depressive Personality Disorder, Self-Defeating Personality Disorder.

My first professional exposure to a person with a personality disorder was with a woman with a Dependent Personality Disorder. This experience became my conversion to what Dr. Christensen was teaching. I accepted the diagnosis of personality disorders, but I did not really believe in the concept of people being unable to change until near the end of my first year of practice. This was true despite the fact that I had identified my mother-in-law as having the symptoms of a personality disorder, and I had no illusions that she was going to change. She was who she was, and my wife and I believed she would not change.

I was very fortunate because people with Dependent Personality Disorder are among the few who will make an effort to get some help. They do this because they have difficulty making decisions and are constantly in need of reassurance. They need people to tell them they are okay and to build them up. This is perfect for what a counselor does with clients. The problem is that when you get to the point where the patient needs to make changes, they are not willing to do so because they are not uncomfortable enough to make the necessary changes.

An acquaintance asked me to meet with his wife; they had two children, and she was a good mother but felt very inadequate. I worked on the usual techniques of improving self-esteem and negative thought patterns. Hard as I tried, though, I could not get her to do the assignments I had given her over eight sessions. I began to feel uneasy because she was always unsure about what to do in many aspects of her life and would fish for compliments from me. I began to feel like she was sticking to me like glue. She was becoming dependent upon me. When I confronted her lack of willingness to follow through with the assignments I had given her she said, "I am going to kill myself." Being conscientious and doing what I was trained to do, I spoke to a colleague in my office, and we took her immediately to a hospital emergency room. While we waited patiently across the hall from the room she was in, a person from the local mental health clinic arrived. He was tasked with assessing if she needed to be admitted to the psychiatric ward. When he left the room he said to his colleague, "She just wants attention. We see her here every now and then." I was embarrassed that I had not detected what she was doing and I realized I was being used. I went back to my office and, after talking to the other staff member, I read the criteria for Dependent Personality Disorder, and she exhibited almost every symptom listed. She did not come back again, and I believe she has probably been to a number of counselors over the years repeating the same process. As I said, I was fortunate to have her come to see me because she helped me understand more about personality disorders. I became more vigilant and paid more attention from then on. You can bet that when I had another person come in who made me feel like he or she was trying to attach to me, I recognized it right away. That is a feeling that possibly some of you have felt when someone becomes overly dependent on you, or it could be someone who dominates your time whenever you bump into him or her. Likely, when you see such a person you feel like hiding or turning around and running the other way. If this is how that person makes you feel, then he or she just might have a personality disorder and the chances he or she will change are not high. That means you will have to do something to adjust, avoid, or just decide to be as pleasant as possible and put up with the behavior. If you confront him or her, the person may react as the individual above did with me.

What Causes Personality Disorders? My Theory

Over the years I have thought about this question and I have come to this conclusion. Each of us is born with a set of personality traits that is unique, and I believe certain people who develop personality disorders are predisposed by sensitivities to rejection, criticism, and many other circumstances that will eventually lead to a full-blown personality disorder. Those who don't slip into a complete diagnosis of a personality disorder may just become depressed and withdraw from life and develop other diagnoses. Some may receive help with medication, therapy, or both and not improve while others will respond positively and recover. In essence, we can see a variety of responses to the same life experiences and environments based on a person's innate personality traits and tendencies.

Parents see the differences in children, even as infants. They recognize early on that this child is easy going and this one is high strung or irritable or one of hundreds of descriptions of personality, temperament, and attitude, etc. Each child is different and this can be measured at an early age. A study was done many years ago, the authors of which I do not recall. The essence of the study was that by five months of age parents were able to identify where their child was on spectrums of nine different personality and temperament traits. An example would be from mild temperament at one end of a spectrum to highly emotional on the other end. The point is that we come with a preprogrammed brain. Some individuals adjust and respond well to negative life experiences and others struggle with the same circumstances. I believe certain individuals are so sensitized to criticism, negative life circumstances, or trauma that when these events occur in life, it triggers such a defensive response that they can never again admit to doing wrong or being wrong to any degree. It is like flipping a switch and hocus pocus, you have a personality disorder. I believe this is accomplished in the subconscious mind, whose job it is to protect us from harm, especially mental-emotional harm. This transformation is so complete that the person makes a conscious decision that he or she will never let anyone else hurt him or her again. Once such individuals step over into this type of mental disorder, there is no turning back; it is complete and, in most cases, final. Now I do believe there are always exceptions to any theory or belief, but they are few and far between when it comes to these disorders. They have their beginnings or onset, as it is referred to, by early adulthood in most cases.

How Do People Who Live and Work with Personality Disordered People Feel?

The Following Is an Account of an Interview with a Family Who Has a Family Member with a Personality Disorder:

On a summer evening not too long ago, I had an entire family who came to see me about a family member. When I opened my door I was surprised to see five family members. Among them was the mother, three of her children, and a granddaughter. All were adults and the granddaughter was in her thirties. They came to tell me about the granddaughter's mother, who was a sibling of the sisters and brother and the daughter of the grandmother. Because this family could not reasonably return again as a group, I spent about two hours with them, and they were on their way, informed and educated with the reality of what a personality disorder was and what the truth was about that person. They also knew what was likely to happen and what was most likely not going to happen.

The specific incident that brought them in was an unfortunate episode which occurred on a rainy evening when the granddaughter (who we will call Betty) was helping her mother (who we will call Joan) with a project in her home. Betty was there out of a desire to get closer to her mother because they had experienced a very rocky and emotional life, full of many rollercoaster rides with outbursts of anger and other inappropriate behavior by her mother, Joan. That evening Joan became highly emotional over something very trivial, and she literally kicked Betty out of the house without her coat or shoes. Luckily, she had her cell phone with her and she called her uncle who was able to pick her up. This was the last straw in a history of many such outbursts she had put up with over many years from her mother. She had finally decided that she could no longer expose herself or her children to this abuse. Remember, this had been going on for her entire life. At this point her aunts and uncle and grand-mother began rehearsing how over the years Joan had become very jealous, suspicious, and resentful to each of them. She had cut off completely one sister, having no contact with her. She had minimal contact with the other sister and the brother was the only one she had some regular contact with about once a month. He had always tried to stay at a distance from her because he had seen how Joan treated her sisters and mother. Any attempts by her sisters to be kind to her were met with more suspicion and contempt and interpreted as malicious toward her. These were loving and kind people who were at the end of their rope after trying to be careful and cautious to not say anything that would upset her. This had been her pattern since she was young, and it became more prominent as she grew older. The grandmother was in a position where she could not say anything positive to Joan about any of the other children, or she would be the recipient of more angry comments. Joan's father, who was not there, had given up on her years ago and felt it was a lost cause. He simply had to let her go, so to speak, because it was too difficult to see how Joan treated the family members.

When they finished, and believe me there was much more to the story than I have room to tell, they thought I would be able to recommend a medication Joan could take to change her behavior. Unfortunately, I had to tell them, "Even if there was a medication for what Joan had, do you really think she would take it?" They had to admit that she would be highly offended if she were offered such a medication even if it was presented in the most pleasant, loving, and innocuous way. They knew how she would react, and it wouldn't be pretty. They had been walking on eggshells around her since she was a teenager, and they found themselves trying to avoid her. The slightest, most diplomatic attempts to interact with her were perceived by her as attacks resulting in intense emotional responses. At times, she could be pleasant but in an instant she could become angry and would attack verbally. They were hoping for a miracle drug to change her behavior to relieve them from the angst of having to deal with her.

What I did was to rehearse to them my introduction to personality disorders by Dr. Christensen and how after my first year of practice I had become a believer. I described to them that people with these disorders do not take personal responsibility for their lives and behavior, and they blame others for their problems in life. I told them I believed Joan had a personality disorder. As I read the symptoms of the possible personality disorders I believed she had, it was like opening a door to a new world for this family. They had the same reaction as do most of my patients upon hearing them; they were astonished and said that I was describing their whole lives with this person. They almost couldn't believe it because the descriptions were so accurate and insightful. Suddenly, they began to realize how difficult it had been to live with her. They continued to describe Joan's behavior in greater detail, leading me to review the symptoms of several other personality disorders, and they all agreed that Joan displayed the majority of symptoms for four of these disorders. This is referred to as a Mixed Personality Disorder because so many symptoms are noted in her behavior. This being the case, Joan had a myriad of behaviors that you don't often see in one person, making it very difficult for anyone to be around her.

People Need to Know the Truth about a Person with a Personality Disorder

Do you see why it is important for the general public to understand that people with personality disorders are everywhere in society today? To know this can make your life less stressful and reduce the pressure of trying to make others happy by letting go of feeling responsible for them.

As I educated these good people about their loved one and how she is mentally ill and will not change no matter what they do, the looks on their faces changed. They began to experience a huge shift in their understanding of life as they had known it with Joan. Her daughter, Betty, decided before she left my office, that she was finally through trying to build bridges with her mother because it always ended in heartbreak for her. She was afraid of further exposing her own children to her mother because there had already been a number of inappropriate interactions in the presence of her children. The other members of the family made similar decisions regarding how they were going to deal or not deal with her.

The Huge Light Bulb Experience

Suddenly, they were thinking new thoughts like, "You mean I don't have to try and make her happy every time I am around her?" "I don't have to be responsible for her and feel guilty for not doing what she wants me to?" "I really can't change her and don't have to feel guilty?" Within that two hour period they went from hoping there was some kind of medication to change her, to nothing we can do will make a difference, and we don't have to make everything better. This is such an enormous leap into the world of reality, which frees people to let go of the accountability they have felt for someone else for most of a lifetime, in some cases. This knowledge also helps them to see that they can decide what they want in terms of a relationship with these people. They can choose to let go and not have contact or anything else they want to do, as long as they realize they can't change the person or make him or her happy.

Whenever I meet with clients who have family members with these diagnoses, it becomes so very rewarding to see how their lives can transform, literally overnight. They become empowered, relieved, and rejuvenated about life, knowing they don't have to enter the "lion's den" anymore. When they do choose to go into that "lion's den," they have a new attitude, one that liberates them to be themselves and to approach the person with a completely different attitude in which they are objective and don't accept the manipulation to take on the other's problems. Of course, if the person we are talking about is a spouse, family member, or someone you live with that is a much more difficult situation to deal with. However, just knowing these facts can be the start of a new way of living your life without all the guilt and confusing emotions you have felt for years.

How Personality Disorders Are Identified/ Diagnosed

If people with personality disorders don't get therapy, then how are they identified or diagnosed? Usually, in my practice, it is when someone comes in who is struggling with someone in his or her life and he or she begins describing that person. I find I can come pretty close to identifying which personality disorder the patient is describing by listening and then asking a few questions. It gets to the point where it is like a familiar tune I hear over and over again, and at that point I pull out the described personality disorder and read the symptoms. It is amazing to see their faces at the recognition of each of the descriptions. They usually indicate that I have just described the person in detail. As I discuss further that these people do not take responsibility for their behavior and place that responsibility in the laps of others, they begin to see the light and understand for the first time what they have been up against for so many years. They also get why the other person won't come in for counseling except possibly once or twice to manipulate the therapist into believing he or she has no problems.

Red Flags That Indicate a Personality Disorder Is Likely

When you hear that someone would not think of seeing a therapist that may be the first red flag. Obviously, there are those who won't go who do not have a personality disorder. However, with the combination of never saying they are sorry, an unwillingness to admit to being wrong, a habit of always blaming others for their problems, and an unwillingness to ever get help, you start to smell something is fishy and further investigation is needed.

Why It Is Important for You to Know about Personality Disorders

Living or working with very difficult people is hard and confusing. It can often cause a person to feel guilty because he or she takes on the responsibility to make the other person happy and cannot figure out how to respond to them because he or she will never know what to say or do to make things better. You are always thinking about how to do things just right to make him or her happy.

When you finally realize that nothing you can do will change them and that they will never change no matter what you do, that is the moment when you can begin to break free from a prison of anger, confusion, and self-doubt. The insight and understanding that follows is such a relief to the individual who has lived in a world of guilt and sadness and experienced feelings of being worn out. It is important to help such an individual realize he or she is a good person and that he or she has been used for the other people's selfish needs.

Individuals who now recognize the reality of their situation finally begin to see that they are not the horrible person they had believed they were. They question their own sanity and motives after being told for so long that they are the one who is crazy, unreasonable, insensitive, unbearable, selfish, and just about every other negative descriptor the affected person can dish out. You cannot change those with a personality disorder; you need to decide how to live with him or her without taking responsibility for his or her happiness and behavior. You need to learn how to live your own life and be happy for yourself. Learn to let go of trying to make that person happy and help others in your family understand the same things so you can all be free together and be on the same page. Support each other and remain strong together.

There Are 10 Main Personality Disorders

The following criteria are from The Diagnostic and Statistical Manual for Mental Disorders, published by the American Psychiatric Association. There have been several versions of this manual over the years and sometime prior to this book being published version V of the DSM will be published. Similar descriptions of these disorders are found at many mental health websites and in many books on mental health subjects. My intent is to inform the general public regarding personality disorders and it is accomplished with the information below from the DSM-IV and in some cases other versions. The criteria in these next pages, is how a psychiatrist, psychologist, social worker, or other mental health professionals make a diagnosis of a personality disorder. These diagnoses are made based on symptoms.

The list of personality disorders begins with an overall or general description of what personality disorders are. The descriptions are a bit technical so you may have to read them carefully.

General Diagnostic Criteria for a Personality Disorder

A) An enduring pattern of inner experience and behavior that deviated markedly from the expectations of the individual's culture. The pattern is manifested in two (or more) of the following areas:

- Cognition (i.e., ways of thinking, perceiving and interpreting self, other people, and events)

- Affectivity (i.e., the range, intensity, lability, and appropriateness of emotional response)

- Interpersonal functioning

- Impulse control

B) The enduring pattern is inflexible and pervasive across a broad range of personal and social situations.

C) The enduring pattern leads to clinically significant distress or impairment in social, occupational, or other important areas of functioning.

D) The pattern is stable and of long duration and its onset can be traced back at least to adolescence or early adulthood.

E) The enduring pattern is not better accounted for as a manifestation or consequence of another mental disorder.

F) The enduring pattern is not due to the direct physiological effects of a substance (e.g., a drug of abuse, a medication) or a general medical condition (e.g., head trauma).

The first three Personality Disorders are categorized according to odd-eccentric behavior dysfunction.

Paranoid Personality Disorder

A) A pervasive distrust and suspiciousness of others such that their motives are interpreted as malevolent, beginning by early adulthood and present in a variety of contexts, as indicated by four (or more) of the following:

- Suspects without sufficient evidence, that others are exploiting, harming, or deceiving him or her

- Is preoccupied with unjustified doubts about the loyalty or trustworthiness of friends or associates

- Is reluctant to confide in others because of unwarranted fear that the information will be used against him or her

- Reads hidden demeaning or threatening meanings into benign remarks or events

- Persistently bears grudges, i.e. is unforgiving of insults, injuries, or slights

- Perceives attacks on his or her character or reputation that are not apparent to others and is quick to react angrily or to counterattack

- Has recurrent suspicions, without justification, regarding fidelity of spouse or sexual partner

B) Does not occur exclusively during the course of schizophrenia, a bipolar disorder or depressive disorder with psychotic features or another psychotic disorder and is not attributable to the physiological effects of another medical condition.

Schizoid Personality Disorder

A) A pervasive pattern of detachment from social relationships and a restricted range of expression of emotions in interpersonal settings, beginning by early adulthood and present in a variety of contexts, as indicated by four (or more) of the following:

• Neither desires nor enjoys close relationships, including being part of a family

• Almost always chooses solitary activities

• Has little, if any, interest in having sexual experiences with another person

• Takes pleasure in few, if any, activities

• Lacks close friends or confidants other than first degree relatives

• Appears indifferent to the praise or criticism of others

• Shows emotional coldness, detachment, or flattened affectivity

B) Does not occur exclusively during the course of schizophrenia, a bipolar disorder or depressive disorder with psychotic features, another psychotic disorder, or autism spectrum disorder and is not attributable to the physiological direct physiological effects of another medical condition.

Schizotypal Personality Disorder

A) A pervasive pattern of social and interpersonal deficits and marked by acute discomfort with, and reduced capacity for, close relationships as well as by cognitive or perceptual distortions and eccentricities of behavior, beginning by early adulthood and present in a variety of contexts, as indicated by five (or more) of the following:

• Ideas of reference (excluding delusions of reference)

• Odd beliefs or magical thinking that influences behavior and is inconsistent with subcultural norms (e.g., superstitiousness, belief in clairvoyance, telepathy, or "sixth sense"; in children and adolescents, bizarre fantasies or preoccupations)

• Unusual perceptual experiences, including bodily illusions

• Odd thinking and speech (e.g., vague, circumstantial, meta-phorical, overelaborate, or stereotyped).

• Suspiciousness or paranoid ideation.

• Inappropriate or constricted affect.

• Behavior or appearance that is odd, eccentric, or peculiar.

• Lack of close friends or confidants other than first degree relatives.

• Excessive social anxiety that does not diminish with famil-iarity. and tends to be associated with paranoid fears rather than negative thoughts about self.

B) Does not occur exclusively during the course of schizophrenia, a bipolar disorder or depressive disorder autism spectrum disorder.

Antisocial Personality Disorder (These people are lifetime criminals)

A) A pervasive pattern of disregard for and violation of the rights of others occurring since age 15 years, as indicated by three (or more) of the following:

• failure to conform to social norms with respect to lawful behaviors. as indicated by repeatedly performing acts that are grounds for arrest.

• deceitfulness, as indicated by repeated lying, use of aliases, or conning others for personal profit or pleasure.

• impulsivity or failure to plan ahead.

- irritability and aggressiveness, as indicated by repeated physical fights or assaults.

- reckless disregard for safety of self or others.

- consistent irresponsibility, as indicated by repeated failure to sustain consistent work behavior or honor financial obligations.

- lack of remorse, as indicated by being indifferent to or rationalizing having hurt, mistreated, or stolen from another.

B) The individual is at least age 18 years.

C) There is evidence of conduct disorder with onset before age 15 years.

D) The occurrence of antisocial behavior is not exclusively during the course of schizophrenia or bipolar disorder.

Borderline Personality Disorder

A pervasive pattern of instability in interpersonal relationships, self-image, and affects, and marked impulsivity, beginning by early adulthood and present in a variety of contexts, as indicated by five (or more) of the following:

- Frantic efforts to avoid real or imagined abandonment. (Note: Do not include suicidal or self-mutilating behavior covered in criterion 5).

- A pattern of unstable and intense interpersonal relationships characterized by alternating between extremes of idealization and devaluation.

- Identity disturbance: markedly and persistently unstable self- image highly or sense of self.

- Impulsivity in at least two areas that are potentially self-damaging (e.g., spending, sex, substance abuse, reckless driving, binge eating). (Note: Do not include suicidal or self-mutilating behavior)

- Recurrent suicidal behavior, or threats, or self-mutilating behavior

- Repeated and rapid mood changes with irritability or anxiety and or lack of joy.

- Constant feelings of emptiness.

- Inappropriate, intense anger or difficulty controlling anger (e.g., frequent displays of temper, constant anger, recurrent physical fights)

- Quickly changing, stress-related paranoid thoughts or severe thoughts not based in reality

Histrionic Personality Disorder

An excessive pattern of emotionality and attention seeking, beginning by early adulthood and present in most areas of life, as indicated by five (or more) of the following:

- Always desiring to be the center of attention

- Interaction with others is often inappropriate sexually or seductive or provocative

- Emotions are often shallow quickly changing

- Uses physical appearance to draw attention to self

- Attempts to impress others with speech but lacks facts and detail

- Dramatizes and exaggerates emotions

- Can be easily influenced by others or circumstances

- Believes relationships to be more intimate than they actually are

Narcissistic Personality Disorder

A pattern of exaggerated behavior or fantasy, need for admiration, and lack of empathy, beginning by early adulthood and present most areas of life, as indicated by five (or more) of the following:

- Has a grand sense of self-importance by exaggerating achievements and talents and expects to be recognized as superior without such achievements

- Constant fantasies of unlimited success, power, brilliance, beauty, or ideal love

- Believes that he or she is "special" and unique and can only be understood by, or should associate with, other special or high status people (or institutions)

- Expects others to give them excessive admiration

- Believes he or she is entitled to unreasonable special treatment and expects others to automatically comply with his or her wants or needs

- Uses, exploits and takes advantage of others to achieve his or her own ends

- Lacks empathy and is unwilling to recognize or identify with the feelings and needs of others

- Is often envious of others or believes that others are envious of him or her

- Is arrogant, egotistical and conceited

Avoidant Personality Disorder

An overall pattern of social inhibition, feelings of inadequacy, and hypersensitivity to possible negative opinion, beginning by early adulthood and present in most areas of life, as indicated by four (or more) of the following:

- Avoids employment that might involve significant interpersonal contact, because of fears of criticism, disapproval, or rejection

- Is unwilling to get involved with people unless certain of being liked

- Limits close relationships because of the fear of being shamed or ridiculed

- Constantly fears being criticized or rejected in social situations

- Is inhibited in new interpersonal situations because of feelings of inadequacy

- Believes he or she is socially incompetent, unappealing, or inferior to others

- Highly reluctant to take personal risks or to engage in any new activities because they may prove embarrassing

Dependent Personality Disorder

An excessive need to be taken care of that leads to submissive and clinging behavior and fears of separation, beginning by early adulthood and present in most areas of life, as indicated by five (or more) of the following:

- Has difficulty making every day decisions without an excessive amount of advice and reassurance from others

- Needs others to assume responsibility for most major areas of his or her life

- Has difficulty expressing disagreement with others because of fear of loss of support or approval. This does not include realistic fears of revenge.

- Has difficulty initiating projects or doing things on his or her own because of lack of self-confidence rather than a lack of motivation or energy

- Goes to great lengths to get positive support from others, to the point of volunteering to do things that are unpleasant

- Feels uncomfortable or helpless when alone because of exaggerated fears of being unable to care for himself or herself

- Quickly seeks another relationship as a source of care and support when a close relationship ends

- Unrealistically fears being left to take care of himself or herself

Obsessive-Compulsive Personality Disorder

An overall pattern of preoccupation with orderliness, perfectionism, personal thought control, the need to control others, at the expense of flexibility, openness, and efficiency, beginning by early adulthood and present in most areas of life, as indicated by four (or more) of the following:

- Is preoccupied with details, rules, lists, order, organization, or schedules to the extent that the major point of the activity is lost

- Perfectionism that interferes with task completion (e.g., is unable to complete a project because his or her own overly strict standards are not met)

- Is excessively devoted to work and productivity to the exclusion of leisure activities and friendships, not because of the need for money

- Is overly conscientious, meticulous, and inflexible about matters of morality, ethics, or values, not accounted for by cultural or religious reasons

• Is unable to throw away worn-out or worthless objects even when they have no real or sentimental value

• Struggles to or will not delegate tasks or work with others unless they submit to exactly his or her way of doing things

• Has a stingy or penny pinching spending style toward both self and others; money is viewed as something to be hoarded for emergencies

• Is rigid and stubborn

Personality Disorder Not Otherwise Specified

This category is for disorders of personality functioning that do not meet criteria for any specific personality disorder. An example is the presence of features of more than one specific personality disorder that do not meet the full criteria for any one personality disorder. This is called a, "Mixed Personality Disorder." This is when the symptoms cause clinically significant problems in social, educational, occupational or other areas of functioning.[6]

Additional Personality Disorders:

There are a few additional Personality Disorders of which you should be aware. Passive aggressive personality disorder was dropped in the DSM-IV from previous versions. Sadistic personality disorder and self-defeating personality disorders were found in the DSM-III-R under proposed diagnostic categories needing further study; however, I believe they are worthy of consideration here. As with the previous personality disorders the descriptions below are described in more understandable terms.

---

6   *Desk Reference to the Diagnostic Criteria from DSM-IV*. P. 275-286. 1994 American Psychiatric Association.

Passive Aggressive Personality Disorder

A pattern of passive resistance toward those who expect normal completion of requests or tasks in social relationships as well as work. This begins by early adulthood and present in most areas of life as indicated by four (or more) of the following:

- Procrastinates by putting off things that need to be done

- Is irritable, sulky and argumentative when asked to do something he or she does not want to do

- Works slowly on purpose or does a poor job when doing something he or she does not want to do

- Complains without legitimate reason that others are expecting too much of him or her

- Avoids obligations and responsibilities by using the excuse of, "forgetting"

- Thinks he or she is doing much better than others perceive

- Resents positive suggestions from others regarding how he or she could do better

- Gets in the way of others by not doing his or her fair share

- Is over critical and puts down those who are in positions of authority [7]

Sadistic Personality Disorder

An all-encompassing pattern of cruel, demeaning, and aggressive behavior, beginning by early adulthood, as indicated by repeated occurrence of at least four of the following:

- Has used physical cruelty or violence to establish dominance in a relationship not just to commit a crime

- Humiliates or ridicules people in the presence of others

---

[7]   *Desk Reference to the Diagnostic Criteria from DSM-III-R.* P. 200. 1987 American Psychiatric Association.

- Treats or disciplines individuals under his or her control unusually harshly including family members and others

- Takes pleasure in, the psychological or physical suffering of others, including animals

- Lies for the purpose of harming or inflicting pain on others, not just to get something they desire

- Gets other people to do what he or she wants through fear, intimidation or even terror

- Controls the freedom of people with whom he or she has a close relationship. Examples are not allowing the spouse to leave the house unaccompanied or permit teenage daughter to attend social functions

- Is fascinated with violence, weapons, martial arts, injury or torture

The behavior above is not directed toward only one person such as a spouse or one child, etc.

This next personality disorder I have seen in a number of victims of long term sexual abuse.

Self-defeating Personality Disorder

An overall pattern of self-defeating behavior, beginning by early adulthood and present in most areas of life. The person avoids or minimizes pleasurable experiences, is drawn to situations or relationships in which he or she will suffer, and prevents others from helping him or her, has indicated by at least five of the following:

- Chooses people and situations that cause disappointment, failure, or mistreatment even when better options are clearly available

- Rejects or minimizes the attempts of others to help him or her

• Following positive personal events or achievements, responds with depression, guilt, or behavior that produces pain

• Causes angry or rejecting responses from others and then feels hurt, defeated, or humiliated such as making fun of someone resulting in an angry response and then feels devastated

• Rejects pleasurable experiences, or is reluctant to acknowledge enjoying himself or herself despite being able to do so

• Fails to do important things crucial to his or her personal objectives despite having the ability to do so, as helping fellow students write papers, but is unable to write his or her own

• Is not interested in or rejects people who treat him or her well. For example, may be unattracted to carrying sexual partners

• Engages in excessive self-sacrifice that is not solicited by the recipients of the sacrifice [8]

This last disorder is not actually included in Personality Disorders; however, I believe it should be noted here so you are aware of it because it is closely associated with personality disorders. This disorder is listed under Impulse Control Disorders in the DSM-IV.

Intermittent Explosive Disorder

• Several aggressive episodes of loss of control that result in serious damage to either persons or property

• The degree of the aggressiveness is very extreme based on the circumstances or provocation

• The violent outbursts cannot be better accounted for by another mental or physical medical condition [9]

---

8   *Desk Reference to the Diagnostic Criteria from DSM-III-R.* P. 214-217. 1987 American Psychiatric Association.

9   *Desk Reference to the Diagnostic Criteria from DSM-IV.* P. 269. 1994 American Psychiatric Association.

Who hasn't seen someone as listed in the above descriptions at least once in their lives?

I believe the following definition of personality disorders as described by the World Health Organization is very insightful into understanding these kinds of people. This is a bit technical but worth reading if you would like more insights into these people.

What Do You Do Now If You Believe a Family Member, Friend or Work Associate Possibly Has a Personality Disorder?

My advice if you think someone in your life has a personality disorder is to:

• Go seek out a counselor-therapist who can assist in helping to diagnose the person. Attempt to get the person to go see the counselor for a diagnosis. (probably won't happen)

• After doing so, discuss this information with other family members or those who may benefit from this knowledge.

• Get some therapy for yourself to assist you in deciding how to deal as effectively as possible with the person.

• Discuss with family or others how to deal with the difficult person so you can support each other on a united front.

Good luck as you decide how to be happy for yourself and avoid falling into the same old pitfalls of being trapped with difficult people in your life.

chapter ten
PSYCHOSIS, SCHIZOPHRENIA AND BIPOLAR DISORDER

In this chapter I am simply describing the symptoms of the above mental disorders. I believe it is important for the public to have a general understanding of them. I have had patients with these disorders, but I do not normally treat them in my practice, with a few exceptions over the years. The reason I do not treat these individuals is because they are very complicated cases requiring psychiatrists and therapists specifically trained in the treatment of these disorders. There is so much more which could be said about these very serious mental disorders, but in the interest of space in this book, I have chosen to be brief yet descriptive enough to give you a basic knowledge. Without question, if anyone you know has these symptoms he or she should be seen by a qualified psychiatrist for proper diagnosis and treatment.

These are severe mental problems and most often require treatment with medication from a psychiatrist. Many of these people are in mental hospitals and treatment centers and require an enormous amount of help and encouragement to stay on medication. It is estimated that approximately 50% of these individuals are homeless adults. You have probably seen them walking on the streets, talking to themselves in a manner that makes no sense.

Psychosis

Psychosis is a condition where the person suffers from a distorted sense of reality. He or she has delusions or beliefs that are not true despite facts that disprove the belief or beliefs. This would include believing he or she has magical talents or other things that cannot stand up to normal reasoning. He or she may also have hallucinations, which consist of seeing things that are not really there nor can they be observed by others. The ability to discern the difference between reality and what he or she thinks and feels is poor. Psychosis is a broad description of people who are not functioning in reality. It is the main component of schizophrenia.

Schizophrenia

The person must have at least two of the following symptoms to qualify for a diagnosis of schizophrenia:

- Delusions

- Hallucinations

- Speech is disorganized, incoherent or monotone

- Strange behavior

- No desire to accomplish things, no pleasure, social withdrawal

There are several different types of schizophrenia. The most commonly known is paranoid schizophrenia, which is manifest in the belief that something or someone is trying to harm the person suffering from the disorder. Another type is called disorganized schizophrenia causing the person to have disorganized speech, behavior, and inappropriate affect or emotional responses or they are lacking in emotional responses. [10]

---

[10] *Desk Reference to the Diagnostic Criteria from DSM-IV.* pp. 147-159. 1994 American Psychiatric Association.

Bipolar Disorder or Manic Depression

Bipolar disorder is also commonly referred to as manic depression, meaning the person alternates between periods of high activity and racing thoughts to depressive feelings and behavior. The person can cycle rapidly through these opposite stages very quickly or slowly. Manic behavior or mania is generally not experienced for longer than one to three days. During the manic stage an individual requires little or no sleep and they come up with all kinds of ideas from strange nonsense to creating inventions or saving the world. It is diagnosed with criteria from the Diagnostic and Statistical Manual of Mental Disorders referred to many times in this book.

Depressive Symptoms

The person must have at least five of the following symptoms of depression for two weeks to qualify for the depressive diagnosis:

- Depressed most of the day almost every day

- Little interest in pleasurable experiences almost every day

- Weight loss (without being on a diet) or gain, because of lack of or increase in a desire to eat

- Too much or not enough sleep almost every day

- Agitated/nervous movements or slowed movements

- Fatigue almost every day

- Feeling worthless or having excessive false guilt almost every day

- Unable to concentrate and or make decisions almost every day

- Thoughts of dying or suicide without making a plan

Manic Episode Symptoms

For at least one week the person has grand, unrestrained thoughts and or irritable mood. The person experiencing these thoughts has great plans to solve some problem or to become rich, etc.

During this week the person has at least three of the following symptoms.

• Exaggerated self-esteem

• Little need for sleep and can feel good after sleeping just three hours

• The person becomes very talkative and continues do so

• Racing thoughts that jump from one subject to another

• Easily distracted by unimportant things

• Becomes highly focused on one activity

• Becomes overly focused on pleasurable actions that can have negative consequences such as spending money, sexual indiscretions, or bad business investments

There is another type of manic episode called hypomanic, in which the person is much less manic than described above, but the person is more manic than what would be normal for him or her. There are several versions of these symptoms, and a person who potentially has them should be seen by a qualified psychiatrist for a diagnosis and treatment. The person can have an episode of just mania or hypomania with depression dispersed between these experiences. There is usually a distinct period when the mania is the main symptom, but it usually subsides for a time and then the depression becomes the greatest concern. Periods of depression usually last longer than the mania or hypomania. The person can cycle through these symptoms rapidly or very slowly over time. It can take many forms and time frames.

This diagnosis can begin before 18 years of age or at any time much later in life. If a person has one episode, it is likely more will follow. I have seen individuals develop this disorder in their early twenties and after retirement. [11]

Causes

All of the above conditions can be caused from heredity, organic factors (neurologic, toxic, and metabolic causes), or the way the brain was formed before birth, or social factors as well as from drugs and alcohol. Having a family member with any of the above diagnoses makes it more likely that a relative might develop the same or similar disorder.

Treatment

These people need treatment from a psychiatrist (for medication) and a therapist (for counseling) trained in dealing with this disorder. Treatment by a team at the same facility would be the ideal here or a psychiatrist and therapist who work together well.

One final note

The above is a thumbnail sketch of these diagnoses and more can be learned if you go to the National Institute of Mental Health (NIMH) and the National Alliance on Mental Illness (NAMI) websites. The above information is for educational purposes and, as with all of the subjects discussed in this book, there is no substitute for a visit with your doctor to get direct and specific help for yourself or a loved one. There may be few or many local resources available to you, and an appointment with your doctor is always advised if you have concerns about the above diagnoses. One of the main problems with those who suffer from these conditions is paranoia, causing the person to distrust

---

11   *Desk Reference to the Diagnostic Criteria from DSM-IV.* pp. 173-183. 1994 American Psychiatric Association.

even close relatives, doctors, and medication. Staying on medications prescribed by their psychiatrist is very important. Those close to individuals with these diagnoses will need a lot of good support from doctors, therapists, family, and friends. Reach out to your doctor and learn all you can if you have a family member with this disorder.

chapter eleven

PSYCHIATRISTS, PSYCHOLOGISTS, PSYCHOTHERAPISTS, SOCIAL WORKERS, WHAT IS THE DIFFERENCE?

There is much misconception and confusion today regarding what is a psychiatrist, psychologist, shrink, psychoanalyst, counselor, etc. Let's get these terms straightened out in our minds once and for all.

What Is a Counselor or a Psychotherapist?

Any type of degreed psychiatrist, psychologist, social worker or other licensed professional can also be called a counselor, psychotherapist or therapist. They all can provide counsel, or do what is called therapy or psychotherapy, all of which falls under the description of counseling. All these terms are used interchangeably, so don't be confused; they essentially mean the same thing, which is helping people change by whatever methodology or type of therapy they chose to practice.

What Is a Psychiatrist?

A psychiatrist is a person who has gone to medical school just like all other doctors who provide medical treatment. Each doctor or physician, as they are referred to, attends medical school to learn the basics of medicine, etc. They eventually have rotations or training in various medical settings like the emergency room, labor and delivery, internal medicine, orthopedics (muscles and bones), surgery, etc.

Toward the later part of their training they need to decide what area or specialty they want to eventually practice in and then they begin specialized training in that discipline, as it is called. One of these specialties is called psychiatry. This is a branch of medicine dealing with mental/emotional disorders. These are medical doctors who specialize in treating patients who are in need of medications for mental illness. Most of these doctors practice in psychiatric hospitals, where they get the majority of their training. Others have practices where they see mostly outpatient clients who are not in the hospital but need to have medication either temporarily or for lifetime. They are experts in what are called psychotropic medications; they regulate and monitor patient medications. There are many other doctors like family practice and OB/GYNs who will prescribe antidepressants or meds for anxiety, etc., but if you or a family member have a more complicated condition, a psychiatrist is the most highly trained doctor with these medications. They can deal with complex drug interactions when more than one medicine is required, which is called poly-pharmacy. There are doctors out there who are not psychiatrists that have high interest and extra training with psychotropic medications who are excellent resources for diagnosing and prescribing medications for mental disorders. There may be such a physician in your area. Inquire with your family doctor regarding who he/she recommends, either for a psychiatrist or a doctor who he/she trusts with these medications. Who knows? You might hit the jackpot. General practitioners are generally easier to get in to see and are less expensive. However, usually they don't have the training psychiatrists receive.

Caution: you will need to know if any of the psychiatrists you plan to see are on your insurance provider list. They are expensive. Depending where you live they may be $200 per hour or more. Psychiatrists are usually booked up, and it is often difficult to get an appointment in a timely manner. It may take a few months, so it would be wise to call for an appointment as soon as you know it is necessary. Doing your homework here is important, including the following questions: Is he/she on your insurance, do you have a co pay, how much will you be charged for the initial evaluation, how much are follow up visits, do they see children, adults, or both, will they arrange payments for services, and any other questions you might have on your mind when calling the doctor's office?

Some examples of conditions they diagnose and treat are depression, anxiety, obsessive compulsive disorder, bipolar disorder, and schizophrenia, as well as all other conditions found in the Diagnostic and Statistical Manual for Mental Disorders. They make a diagnosis and, if it is necessary, they send you off with a prescription and many recommend other treatments as well. You will probably be told to return from within a month to three months for a 15 minute follow up appointment to evaluate how the medications are working. This interview is much less expensive, making a psychiatrist more affordable provided there are no excessive complications with interactions and tolerance, etc. After a patient is stabilized on a medication, they may not have to return for 6 months to a year depending on what medications they are taking. It is possible that the diagnostic interview, as it is called, may need to be extended to an additional appointment if the case requires further information or possibly either medical tests or psychological testing from a psychologist.

Do Psychiatrists Provide Counseling or Therapy?

This leads me to the one thing that everyone should know about psychiatrists. Most psychiatrists do not do therapy or counseling. There are some areas of the country where they do, but this is very expensive and most people can't afford them, especially if treatment goes on for several months or longer. Some people assume they will be getting emotional support when they see a psychiatrist; however, you should not expect this because he or she will be asking a lot of questions to get to a diagnosis, which does not leave a lot of time for "warm fuzzies." The same will be true in your follow up appointments. These are information gathering interviews, so a patient should avoid feeling disappointed if it seems like they are a package on a conveyer belt.

What Is a Psychologist?

A psychologist has received a bachelor's degree, usually in psychology and then they go on to graduate school for a period of 3 to 4 years depending on the type of degree and school they attend. There are many types of psychologists with different training. When they finish school they have what is called a Ph.D. (doctorate) and, after attaining this degree, they are referred to as a doctor of psychology. For example, Dr. Phil, as I understand, has a Ph.D. in Organizational Psychology. This is a branch of psychology that studies how employees, workplaces and organizations operate. Two of the most common branches of Psychology families become involved with are called Counseling Psychology and Clinical Psychology. Counseling Psychology teaches and trains students in theories and methods of counseling. A Clinical Psychologist performs evaluations for all kinds of disorders and learning disabilities, and they may or may not do counseling. They have a number of tests that can determine much about a person such as depression, anxiety, ADHD, I.Q. (intelligence testing), even developmental levels in children and much more. Today there is a great need for psychologists who can test for autism, and not all psychologists have the training to do this. There are psychologists who have one to two years of training and their degrees are called Master's Degrees. They are called Psychologists, but in some cases they need a Ph.D. psychologist to review and sign off on their reports in order to be paid by insurance or to be recognized as acceptable in different areas of the country. Many of these master's-level psychologists are excellent and have years of experience.

Counseling Psychologists are those who chose to do therapy. They may be Ph.D.'s with a three or four-year degree or they might be a master's degree psychologist. Different states or nations will license these professionals according to local laws. Some states may not allow master's-degreed psychologists to have a private practice, yet they may be allowed to practice under the supervision of a Doctor of Psychology (Ph.D.) or with an agency which is legally licensed. Examples of this would be local mental health offices which have a variety of therapists on staff who are allowed to do therapy under the umbrella of the agency. They usually are supervised by other credentialed therapists who may not be psychologists.

Other Kinds of Psychologists

There are other kinds of psychologists who practice psychotherapy, and they come from a variety of educational backgrounds. Some receive their education from schools of educational psychology. You may have had contact with these psychologists in the school system. Some may be School Psychologists or School Counselors. They can be either master's level psychologists or the three to four year degreed psychologists whose credentials are generally spelled Ed.D. meaning a Doctor of Educational Psychology The initials can be somewhat different depending on the school they attend and their training or specialty. I have known therapists who have degrees in Recreational Psychology and other psychologists in related fields. The main thing to remember is that there are many kinds of practicing psychologists, so you would be well-served by asking what kind of degree, experience, and what type of therapy they do before making a decision regarding a counselor.

Please take note that a good psychologist does not necessarily have to have a doctorate degree. I know several psychologists with master's degrees who are excellent clinicians. The term "Clinician" means one who does counseling or therapy or testing.

I personally have worked with a number of psychologists who test children for various kinds of mental/emotional disorders from learning problems to autism. About half of these psychologists are doctorate-level psychologists with Ph.D.'s and the rest are master's level psychologists. My experience with both groups of psychologists is all positive. I have every confidence in these professionals, and I would not hesitate to refer patients to them. However, be cautious because not everyone will be competent, just as in all other walks of life, there will be those who practice a profession who are not as good as others. This reality makes it very important for you to do your homework and be prudent who you chose to go to.

What Is a Psychoanalyst?

A psychoanalyst is a person who has received extensive training in psychoanalytic theory/therapy developed by Sigmund Freud. Anyone from a psychiatrist to a psychologist, social worker, or other related fields of study can be trained in this methodology. The majority of psychoanalysts are found in the Eastern United States and others are scattered in many places and nations. This is usually a type of therapy that requires a lot of time with the therapist. Finances are, therefore, an important consideration. If you're comfortable with Freud and his theories you may want to consider a psychoanalyst. If you are unaware of his theories and are interested, go to the library or do some research online. Most states do not license and regulate psychoanalysts which is why it is important to ask questions about the degrees and training the psychoanalyst has. Psychoanalysts cannot prescribe medication unless they are also a psychiatrist.

What Is a Shrink?

In the past a "Shrink" meant a psychiatrist. More recently the consensus seems to be that this term is associated with any kind of mental health counselor.

What Is a Social Worker?

Social workers can have a bachelor's degree, master's degree, or Doctor of Social Work Degree. Social workers do all kinds of jobs from protecting children and adults as part of state and local agencies to foster care to therapy of all kinds. They work in hospitals and many other types of settings. Many have private counseling practices and others work in mental health centers. Probably the most common therapists in mental health facilities are social workers. Some have bachelor's degrees and can do therapy under the agency license. They are supervised by higher degreed individuals. Master's degree social workers are authorized to have private practices in most states, and there are many thousands who do therapy throughout the country. Agencies licensed to provide services to children are required to have a master's degree social worker on staff in most states. There are many thousands of Licensed Clinical Social Workers (titles vary depending on locations) who are excellent psychotherapists throughout the nation and other parts of the world. They must be licensed in their states and are required to maintain several hours of training per year to keep their license in force. This is the case with all other licensed counselors regardless of their degrees.

Other Licensed Counselors

There are other counselors who are also licensed by states to do therapy. These vary between states and countries. Some are Licensed Professional Counselors, Marriage and Family Therapists, Mental Health Professionals, and more, depending on where you live. You can obtain names of these licensed counselors by contacting your local or state professional licensing department. Because they are licensed, they must have certain kinds of education, supervision, and current training. Being licensed by a state or government usually means that these professionals have an education, training, and is up-to-date regarding new developments in his or her field. Therefore, they are deemed to be competent in providing clients with counseling.

chapter twelve

MEDICATION FOR MENTAL HEALTH TREATMENT

The reason for medication in the treatment of mental health is simple. Some people are so depressed, anxious, etc. or have dysfunction of the brain to the extent that they are in need of something to balance brain function. If they are able to benefit from counseling, the medication may enable them to more effectively utilize skills they learn in therapy. In serious cases of brain dysfunction such as bipolar disorder and schizophrenia, medication can make the difference between someone who can function socially and possibly even maintain employment and an individual who is unable to interact within the confines of reality.

Psychotropic Medications

A significant number of people who are on the street and frequent homeless shelters have the diagnosis of either bipolar disorder or schizophrenia. These people could be much more productive in society if they would stay on medication. Their problem is that many don't like the way the medication makes them feel, even though they function better. They begin to experience a degree of paranoia and think someone is trying to manipulate them, harm them, or they conjure up some kind of conspiracy story to give reason why they should not take medication. They can also have what is called anosognosia which is a lack of awareness that they have a serious mental health problem. Another problem many of these people face is when they are doing better on medication they have a tendency to believe they don't need medication anymore, and they stop taking it. The family sees the changes and wonders what is happening, and they may have little effect in an attempt to get him or her to go back on meds. The sad fact is that if the person suffering were to stay on medication, he or she is more able to maintain employment and social appropriateness. A number of years ago I took a tour through a facility with a program designed to encourage these folks to stay on their medications. The building had a cafeteria, a treatment area where groups and individuals were being seen by staff, and a sheltered workshop where these people could create or repair items to be sold in a small store on the premises. This was a great way to keep these people on meds and off the street where they were at risk for all kinds of problems from being victims of violence, exposure to severe weather, and little or no nutrition. The key for these people is to keep them on medication so they are able to operate much better in society.

There is also the possibility of people who are on too many medications or the wrong dosages, and this can be a real problem in terms of functioning at work, in the home with children, at school, and socially. It is important for close family members to have access to the doctor, with the patient's permission, so they can give feedback regarding how the patient is functioning. If possible, it is wise to have a family member accompany the patient to appointments with the doctor to provide this important and objective input about how he or she is doing on the medications. It will be necessary to sign a release of medical information at the doctor's office so this can be done, unless the patient is a minor child.

Who Treats These People?

Doctors who treat these individuals are called psychiatrists. They are trained to diagnose patients and treat them with what are called psychotropic medications and most do not do therapy. If you have a family member who has a severe mental-emotional problem requiring medication, a psychiatrist is the type of medical doctor he or she should be treated by. There are other medical doctors who have interest in and training with psychotropic medications. Your primary care physician may know of such doctors who may be easier to get in to see than psychiatrists. Where I live it can take two to four months to get an appointment with a psychiatrist.

There are several classifications of psychotropic medications which can be effective treatments for mental illness. The following describes some of these drugs and what they are used for.

A Word about Medication Side Effects and Risks

As with all medications there are possible risks and possible side effects. Every person's brain is different; therefore, they respond differently to medications, some having no problems while others might have mild to severe reactions. This is why it is critical to discuss with your doctor these issues before you take the step into this type of treatment. There are all kinds of rumors circulating about the evils of medication. I hope you will be open to considering a balanced approach to this matter. People with health problems take medications for their conditions which makes life less difficult and more productive. Take, for instance, someone with diabetes who is on insulin. Does his or her doctor say, "Just tough it out and learn to live with it," or is medication recommended because to not treat would mean painful and life-threatening complications? Each organ in the human body is delicate and prone to dysfunction, depending on an individual's genetics and how well he or she takes care of himself or herself. The brain is the most complicated organ in the body, and it is folly and illogical to assume the brain is not capable of malfunction requiring medication.

If you or a family member is placed on a medication, you need to make sure that you work as a team giving feedback from the patient and perceived observations from the family to the doctor about any side effects or questions. This is when adjustments or a change in medication becomes necessary. This is a must!

Antipsychotics

Examples are Haldol, Thorazine and Mellaril.

These types of drugs are used for the treatment of schizophrenia and mania. Schizophrenia is a serious mental illness causing a person difficulty with thinking clearly and making rational decisions. Psychosis or delusions and hallucinations are experienced by the person in which voices are heard and things are seen that are not real. Speech and behavior can be disorganized and the person's ability to function appropriately in society is impaired.

Mania is behavior characterized by excessive self-esteem, lack of need for sleep, excessive talk, racing thoughts, irritability or euphoria, surges of energy, pleasure seeking, and increased risk-taking behavior. This behavior is part of what is called bipolar disorder, sometimes called manic depressive disorder.

With these types of behaviors, therapy is not as successful as in other less severe diagnoses. This is why medications are sometimes the only viable treatment option.

Atypical Antipsychotics

Examples are Abilify, Risperdal and Seroquel.

These are newer drugs designed for the treatment of the same schizophrenia and mania as described above under antipsychotics. Some are used to treat extreme moods and difficult behaviors.

Mood Stabilizers

Examples are Depakote, Lithium and Lamictal.

These medications are used for treatment of bipolar disorder also known as manic depression. It is characterized by extreme highs and lows of mood. Highs might include extreme energy, lack of need for sleep, spending sprees, or impulsive acts such as quitting a job. Lows may be described as deep depression, long episodes of sleep, hopelessness, and guilt over debt and loss of job, etc.

People with bipolar disorder are more likely to benefit from psychotherapy than those with schizophrenia.

Antidepressants

Examples are Elavil, Norpramin, Prozac, Zoloft, Celexa, Nardil, Effexor and Wellbutrin.

These medications are self-explanatory as they treat depression. Some have been around for many years and some are newer and have different mechanisms to affect brain function. Your doctor can explain how they work.

The older antidepressants are called MAO inhibitors and Tricyclics. Newer ones are called Selective Serotonin Reuptake Inhibitors (SSRIs) and atypical antidepressants.

How Selective Serotonin Reuptake Inhibitors and Some Atypical Antidepressants Work

Below is a very basic depiction of how some of these newer antidepressants work. This diagram is typical of drugs like Prozac, Zoloft, Celexa and other Selective Serotonin Reuptake Inhibitors. In the white matter of the brain, which consists of the wiring, there are spaces or voids between the pre-synaptic and post-synaptic nerve endings called the synapse. When signals come down these pathways they must jump across the synapse on what are called neurotransmitters to be received on the other side by receptors, thus completing the transmission of the signal to where it is supposed to go. When someone becomes depressed there are less of these neurotransmitters available to carry these messages across the synapse. The reason for this phenomenon is not completely understood. One of these neurotransmitters is called serotonin and is specifically targeted by SSRIs or Selective Serotonin Reuptake Inhibitors to prevent the absorption of serotonin. As the name implies, the medication selectively works on serotonin and reuptake is another word for absorption. Therefore, these medications inhibit the reuptake process, which, over time, increases the amount of serotonin in the synapse, thereby providing a more normal level of serotonin to send and receive messages in the brain. These drugs do not create more serotonin and that is why it takes time for levels to rise; two to six weeks is the common timeframe. There are other neurotransmitters in the brain, and some of the other antidepressants work on them in like manner.

Wiring of the Brain

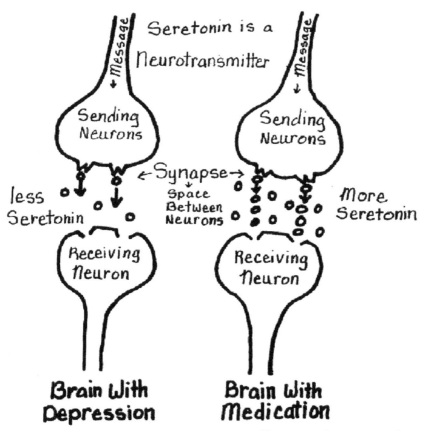

Illustration by Matt Anderson

Depression causes low levels of Serotonin in the wiring of the brain. SSRI medication increases these Serotonin levels by preventing Serotonin from being absorbed. Reuptake is another word for absorption.

Anti-Panic Agents

These medications are Klonopin and Paxil and are for panic attacks.

Anti-Obsessive Agents

Examples are Anafranil, Luvox, Paxil, Prozac, and Zoloft.

These drugs offer help for those who have obsessive compulsive disorder, more common today than you would think.

Antianxiety Agents

Examples are Lexapro, Ativan, Valium and Xanax.

Obviously, these medications help patients who have various forms of anxiety.

Stimulants

Examples are Adderall, Cylert, Ritalin and Vivance.

These medications treat attention deficit disorder and attention deficit hyperactivity disorder.

I hope this information is useful in opening up the window of understanding so you can talk to your doctor with a more informed perspective. Good luck.

chapter thirteen

COUNSELING OR PSYCHOTHERAPY: WHAT IS IT AND WHO DOES IT?

Counseling and Psychotherapy are terms used interchangeably, so when I say one or the other they are the same.

Let's Demystify Psychotherapy by Explaining What it is and How it is Done.

In its simplest terms counseling or psychotherapy means to do whatever we have to do to get a person to where he or she wants to be. In other words, you decide what you want out of counseling and our goal will be to get you there. In most, if not all cases, we will need to diagnose what the problem is so we can better identify a solution. This solution is called a treatment plan. Treatment plans are basic and simple because they have two components. The first is education and the second is gaining insight into why we do what we do. I tell my clients that therapy consists of me teaching them information and concepts just like they were going to a seminar or a workshop. The only difference is that we will be doing this one-on-one instead of in a group. There is no mind control or hocus pocus, just plain common sense education regarding the use of proven methods to change one's thinking to be more accurate and objective. In addition, I tell my clients that this process of counseling is insight therapy where, through the above process, we gain insights about ourselves.

Your First Step

The first thing you have to do is determine who you will go see. There are three ways of doing this; the first thing to do if you have insurance is to check your insurance company's mental health provider list to find out who they will pay for you to go see. There usually is a mental health phone number to call on the reverse side of your insurance card. Ask how many sessions or appointments they allow. Some insurance companies may not have a provider list, and they allow you find your own provider. In this case the second option is to ask friends or family members if they know anyone they would recommend. The third is to look in the phone book or online for counselors. Counselors can be psychologists, social workers, marriage and family therapists, and also licensed counselors who may have degrees in other related fields. Some of these counselors may have a bachelor's degree and work with an agency. Most states require counselors who have private practices to have at least a master's degree in psychology, social work, or related fields of study. I go into detail about the differences between these professions in the chapter on PSYCHIATRISTS, PSYCHOLOGISTS, PSYCHOTHERAPISTS, SOCIAL WORKERS, WHAT IS THE DIFFERENCE?

Next is calling and asking these counselors if they work with people who have your specific concerns. By this I mean individual counseling for depression, anxiety, marriage counseling, dealing with children's behavior problems, etc.

The next thing you will probably want to find out is how much the fee is in terms of your co-pay. If you are paying all fees out of pocket, ask if they require the money up front or if they allow you to make payments.

Finding a counselor and the fees involved are addressed in more detail within other chapters of this book.

How Long Does Counseling Take, and How Often do I Need to Go? What Are Short Term and Long Term Therapy?

Short term therapy is generally defined as 12 sessions or less. Sometimes this is called brief therapy. Unless someone is really struggling, most therapists see patients once per week. Many patients can complete therapy within that timeframe. I see patients, for the most part with "average" concerns, from approximately 3 to 8 sessions, the most common being about five sessions. When I say average concerns I mean excluding victims of long-term abuse, eating disorders, or other very complicated problems. These longer term patients may need to be seen for months or in some cases much longer. Long term therapy can be defined as lasting for a minimum of three months, or in less frequent cases, years. Many conditions such as minor depression, low self-esteem, anxiety and marriage problems not on the verge of divorce, can be resolved within the short term timeframe of 12 sessions.

Some therapy methods such as psychoanalysis can go on for years. This seems to be less the case presently but there are certain areas of the country where this is still common.

There are Three Categories of Therapy

These categories are simplified ways of illustrating the kinds of therapy people might need.

Supportive therapy

Some of us only need supportive therapy to balance out our thinking to the point where we can utilize our own abilities to resolve our own difficulties. This is a category where most people who are dealing with stressful situations in life will be. Some people get along well by talking to family or friends, and they figure out how to adjust and carry on. Some go to counselors to get help.

Cognitive therapy

This is a broad term to describe the kind of therapy people need if they have been under so much stress and/or difficulty that their thinking processes have been altered and they do not know how to return to a proper way of thinking. This requires a little longer period of therapy to assist the person to become more objective and logical in his or her thinking. Thus it is called cognitive or thinking therapy. Sometimes this type of therapy needs to be accompanied with the application of medication, either for a short period of time or possibly longer. People who fall into this category have been exposed to life stressors for longer periods of time and therefore need a little longer to change their thinking, make different decisions, and adjust to their stressors.

Long-term Therapy

People who need long term therapy have complicated and very severe mental-emotional problems, which can be caused by extreme experiences such as sexual abuse, physical abuse, or even torture, war and other forms of extreme treatment by others, etc. Being involved in life threatening natural disasters can also require long term treatment. Genetics can also have great impact on this as well. These individuals are the most severely affected people who generally need medication and therapy, sometimes lifelong. This is a smaller population of people who need of this kind of help.

I read a statement from someone years ago and I do not remember who he was so I am paraphrasing his words. Some people become so confused, are so badly mistreated by parents or spouses, engage in inappropriate behaviors or become mentally ill to such an extent that they are unable to make personal decisions and exercise their own free will. In these cases, sometimes the right professional person is necessary to help these folks stabilize their lives sufficiently to enable them to make better choices. If the problems are serious enough, sometimes they need medication to get them to a point where they can begin to feel enough confidence to apply the new skills they learn in therapy and then go on to make their own decisions.

Counselor or Psychotherapist

The Counselor can also be called a Psychotherapist. These terms are interchangeable and essentially mean the same thing.

What Kind of Counselors Are There?

Much of the counseling in this country is done by social workers like me. Many social workers have a designation called Clinical Social Workers or Licensed Clinical Social Workers. This means they have acquired a certain level of training, hours of practice and competency to receive this designation. I am licensed in my state as Licensed Clinical Social Worker. This means I can operate a private practice, and it is the highest professional licensure for social workers in the state. I am also a Board Certified Diplomate in Clinical Social Work through the American Board of Examiners in Clinical Social Work. Social workers, as well as psychologists and other counseling professionals, are regulated and licensed to protect the public and make sure therapists are educated and properly trained. If these professionals are licensed within their state, they have permission to practice and have met required professional criteria and would be considered competent to provide counseling. To learn more about counselors check out the chapter on PSYCHIATRISTS, PSYCHOLOGISTS, PSYCHO-THERAPISTS, SOCIAL WORKERS: WHAT IS THE DIFFERENCE?

The First Session: What You Might Expect

I have the client/patient (they mean the same thing) fill out an application questionnaire to get information about him or her. This will include how the patient proposes to pay plus insurance information. This can be tricky because insurance programs have lots of rules, and you may need to get a preauthorization from them. After we agree on the financial and insurance matters and take care of the co-pay, we go on to the next step. In my private practice I allow patients to set up payments to suit their financial needs if that is necessary. If you are going to a larger counseling office you will most likely be taking care of the financial matters with a secretary who will ask for your co-pay, fee or for payment arrangements. The application questionnaire also asks about the symptoms or problems the patient is experiencing. You may also have to sign an agreement that if you contemplate suicide you will contact the therapist immediately or call 911.

Information Gathering and Diagnosis

After reviewing what they have written, I then ask them what they are here for today and give them a chance to verbalize in their own words what they want to accomplish in therapy. A history of the problem and of their lives is taken and if they have sought counseling previously. Are they taking medicine, or do they have any medical problems? I give them enough time to say what is on their minds until they become more comfortable and have said all they want to say.

After asking a number of questions, I attempt to formulate a theory or diagnosis so we can determine what kind of treatment the person/s will need. The questions I ask come from a book called the DSM-IV: The Diagnostic and Statistical Manual for Mental Disorders. Sometimes I have patients fill out questionnaires to get a lot more information a little faster. Depending on the diagnosis, there can be a spectrum of symptoms from mild to severe. By understanding how severe the symptoms are I will know if a consultation from a physician is required to determine if medication is appropriate.

In severe cases, if they are in danger of hurting themselves, others or property, some kind of intervention will be needed. This may require a visit to the emergency room if they are willing to go voluntarily, or if they are not willing or able to make a choice, a call to 911 may be in order. I know there are people who will read this and begin to panic because they are terrified to go to the hospital or mental health facility.

They fear losing control or being away from the safety of their home. They ask themselves, "Who will take care of the children or the responsibilities at work? How will I pay for it because I have too many debts and I have no way to pay because I have inadequate insurance?" I explain to patients in this situation that in most cases this will be temporary and they will be alive to take care of their family when they have finally dealt with their issues. For now, the most important thing is to get them help so they will remain alive. There are ways for hospitals to reduce your financial responsibility and in many cases, if you have no insurance, the bill can be written off. Ask and you may be very surprised.

Establishment of a Relationship between the Counselor and the Client

The relationship between the client and therapist begins from the first session and continues to change throughout the duration of the therapy. This relationship ideally becomes one of trust and respect between them, requiring complete honesty from both. Strong feelings can develop between them and this is why a professional relationship must always be maintained.

Working Stage

This stage will involve exploring with the client how misinterpreted situations in life create errors in thinking and perception. The ideal is that the client begins to get insights into how he or she came to be in such a difficult situation. This helps the patient to learn how to avoid similar triggers in the future. This is when I teach awareness of thinking distortions and describe methods of coping, and skills to change faulty thought patterns to the client. There are many methods that are used by counselors today which are appropriate and acceptable to accomplish this end.

I almost always give my clients assignments when they leave each session. They need more than just a 50 minute session per week.

Obviously, if they are doing something that is helping them to change their thinking and behavior on a daily basis their progress will accelerate. To explain this in a humorous way, I like the way someone once put it, "One day for church, six for fun, chances of getting to heaven, six to one."

Another reason I give assignments is to help clients work on changes in their own world. Many are more comfortable trying these new skills in the safety of the environment they know best, such as home, work or play. Some clients feel more comfortable working on them in my office and, if so, we work on them there until they are able to take them outside to real life situations. I also want these people to begin seeing success and thus the rewards become fun and exciting. This translates to hope and more success. I really look forward to hearing a person say something like, "I never knew I was so hard on myself until I started doing this exercise." When patients start to understand how they got where they are in life this is called Insight Therapy. This is a very important part of the Working Stage, getting your own insights about you. I once read a book called, The Inner game of Tennis, by Timothy Gallwey. He described having lunch one day at a tennis club on a terrace outside the clubhouse. The windows were treated with a reflective material giving them the quality of a mirror. A gentleman recognized him and asked if he would give him some pointers because his tennis game was miserable. He was a little irritated at first but eventually asked him to demonstrate his swing, and it was pretty bad. Then an idea came to him to have him look in the mirrored window and observe his own swing. Upon viewing his own reflection he was able to correct his swing as he practiced in the mirror. Within no time he was swinging much better and essentially he cured his own tennis game. Although it is much more difficult for clients to do their own therapy, they can receive insights and impressions which can change their outlook on life encouraging greater efforts at self-change.

Termination

Once clients have learned how to recognize the triggers causing their distress, and in many cases how they originated, they learn how to use cognitive or thinking skills to reduce their faulty perceptions. As they become more competent in applying these skills, they gain confidence and realize they are more in control of their life. Somewhere through this process they gain insights into how they were instrumental in keeping their distortions intact. This helps them to become more self-aware, which is called "mindfulness" nowadays. They become better able to "self-regulate," another current term used today to describe changing the way they think and act. When this corner is turned the client and therapist usually know it is time to begin terminating the counseling by extending appointments to every other week, after which a decision is made to terminate the therapy. This is a natural process and both the individual and therapist can sense when it is time to let him or her take on life with these new skills in place. This is a great moment in therapy and one I look forward to, when essentially the client says, "I don't need you anymore; I know how to do this."

I hope I have helped to make therapy or counseling a little less intimidating and hopefully those who need it will take the steps to change their lives for the better.

HOW TO FIND A THERAPIST OR COUNSELOR

How to Find a Therapist or Counselor

If you have health insurance with mental health coverage, then contact them for a list of mental health providers they will allow you to see. You may want to check with your primary care physician who may be familiar with therapists accepted by your insurance, which he or she trusts. Potentially your insurance company may not have the therapist you want to work with on their list of providers. In such cases you may have to pay for all your therapy if you choose to go to a therapist who is out of network, meaning not on your insurance company's provider list. You may very well have a mental health phone number to call for preauthorizations on the reverse side of your insurance card. Some insurance companies provide members with a booklet which lists mental health providers in your area. Other insurances may only provide a list on the Internet, which you can download to your computer. You should inquire if a preauthorization is required prior to making an appointment. If you are able to preauthorize your first appointment, the chances of having to pay the entire fee will be reduced.

Before you start contacting prospective providers, please be aware that most insurance companies will not pay for marriage counseling. They will usually only pay their part of the fee if you are given a mental health diagnosis after an evaluation with a counselor. A diagnosis would be such conditions as depression, anxiety, obsessive compulsive disorder, posttraumatic stress disorder or any of many other diagnoses found in a manual called the DSM-V. This is the Diagnostic and Statistical Manual for Mental Disorders. Every mental health professional should have this manual because it lists all of the mental health disorders people experience. Your insurance carrier will have their own specific rules regarding what types of diagnoses they are willing to cover. It might be helpful when you first call the insurance company to tell them generally why you are seeking counseling so they can tell you if your counseling will be covered. This may be uncomfortable for some people and unfortunately this might prevent them from seeking help. You will never see these insurance representatives and they will not know you so don't let this stop you. Most of the people you will talk to will not be in your city or state. The insurance company will almost always say that the conversation with you is not a guarantee of coverage. This can be a little tricky so be smart and take notes.

Some insurance companies do not have lists of providers, so you can go to anyone you like. Depending on the coverage your company has you may be responsible for a small co-pay or for 50% or more of the fees for counseling. Ask who you can see and what fees you are responsible for when you call the mental health preauthorization number on your insurance card. If they allow you to see anyone you chose then it may be up to you to find a counselor because they might not have a provider list. There are some insurance plans that require you to only go to their facility where they have counselors on staff. The bottom line here is that if you have insurance and you want to go to a certain counselor, the chances are that they may not pay for you to see him or her. In order to see the counselor of your choice you may need to pay the fees yourself. This is where negotiating for payments that fit your ability to pay can be very important. Don't be afraid to ask about this!

If you are on your own to find a counselor, you can look in the phone book for counselors or do a search online for the same in your area. You can search for clinical social workers, psychologists, and marriage and family therapists to see what comes up. Some states have lists of these same professionals in their department of professional licensing, so you can try that kind of a search also. This would assure that you are seeing someone who is licensed. You can also try looking on national registers for these professions. "Find a Psychologist," is a website that is helpful; there are also several registers such as The National Association of Social Workers, The American Board of Examiners in Clinical Social Work, The American Psychological Association and The Association for Marriage and Family Therapy. These are all good places to start.

Authorizing Evaluations and Therapy Sessions

As mentioned above, you will need to call your insurance's mental health authorization line to receive permission to see a therapist. You may be given an authorization number to take with you to the first appointment. If this is the case, make sure you write it down and take it with you. Many insurance companies will authorize from two to six sessions initially for an evaluation and follow up appointments. Some insurance companies may authorize only an initial evaluation and will require the therapist to contact them for additional sessions after reviewing the diagnosis and treatment plan. Some plans, depending on the type of insurance package you have, may authorize three to as many as 20 or more sessions per year, per incidence of the same diagnosis. If this is the case, they may require the therapist to submit the progress notes and/or updated treatment plans at certain predetermined points along the way. If you max out the total sessions allowed, they might require the therapist to submit reasons why therapy should go beyond the maximum along with another treatment plan, if it is necessary. If they will not pay beyond this limit you may have to pay for the remaining appointments.

What Kind of Counseling Will Insurance Companies Pay for?

As indicated earlier, insurance companies will pay for patients to see a counselor if they have a diagnosis like depression or anxiety and others, but most do not pay for marriage counseling. Very often, however, in my experience as a therapist, at least one or both of the spouses who are seeking therapy have symptoms of depression or other mental-emotional conditions that may qualify for a diagnosis the insurance company will accept for payment. This is why it is important to diagnose both spouses when they come for treatment. If a qualifying diagnosis is made for either spouse, treatment may require individual therapy as well as marriage therapy because the marriage may be the cause of the diagnosis of depression, etc. It is up to the therapist to decide what to do in terms of a treatment plan. So even though insurance companies do not pay for marriage counseling directly, they will pay for the treatment of depression, anxiety, etc. and part of the resulting treatment may be marriage counseling.

Employee Assistance Programs

A note about Employee Assistant Plans or EAP as they are called. They are also referred to as Employee Assistant Programs. These are programs some companies provide their employees and their families. They receive professional help for individual therapy, marriage therapy or any diagnoses, regardless of what they are. Sometimes employees are referred to these resources to avoid disciplinary measures or as a method of helping a problem at home or work from getting out of control, thus avoiding disciplinary action or termination. Some companies require updates to the immediate supervisor of the employee and other companies turn a blind eye and don't want to meddle in what is being done, especially if the treatment has nothing to do with work performance. This is a great way to get help for your family if your employer offers it. These programs will usually offer from two to eight sessions free of charge. You can check this out by contacting your Human Resources office. If you need therapy beyond the allowed number of sessions, you will be referred back to your mental health benefits through your insurance plan.

What to Ask When Shopping for a Counselor

The next step is yours to do some calling and asking questions to determine who you will make an appointment with. As with any profession or business, you can find poor, fair, good, great or excellent people in counseling. When you are looking for a doctor, you ask a lot of questions before you chose one. The same holds true for counselors; ask around about who have good reputations before making an appointment. Inquiring about their years of experience, specialties and ages they serve are all important questions to ask when choosing a therapist. As you ask around you may be surprised how many of your acquaintances know counselors. Don't be afraid to ask; there is nothing to lose unless you are the type who would rather lose your family, child, marriage or sanity rather than your pride. By the time you need help, many of the people in your world are probably aware something is wrong, and if they are real friends they will want to help.

What Not to Ask

Early in my career, I received a phone call from a potential client who asked me questions about my experience, and he eventually said he wanted someone who had at least eight children and had been practicing for 20 years. I wanted to say, "What if the person you are describing has the children and the 20 years but is a lousy therapist?" I did say don't limit yourself with a therapist by placing prerequisites about his or her life experiences. He did not come in, and I would guess he had an adventure finding the right counselor for the job. I even talked to a woman one time who said her husband would not see a therapist unless he had been in the Vietnam War and had the same experiences in combat as he had. She believed no one could help him unless that person had been through the same experiences. The truth is, no one we go to will ever have the same experiences we have, so if that is our philosophy, we will be out of luck. The point being, if we want to change, there is someone out there who can help us with those changes. We do need a counselor who will listen and understand us. Without this quality, we will have no confidence in her or him and will probably not go back. If the therapist allows us to share our inner-self and we sense that he or she is truly trying to understand, we will feel a sense of relief and will start to trust. This is how a positive client/ therapist relationship will develop. If a therapist jumps in and starts giving direction and advice without establishing a relationship then most likely the client will feel just as misunderstood in that setting as he or she does in the world outside therapy. This is unfortunate because the client may get the message that counseling does not work.

If you have a poor experience in therapy, give someone else a try just as you would with a doctor. You may have had a less than positive exam with a doctor, but I hope you did not give up and instead found someone else you are comfortable with. I ask you to think the same way with counselors. A study was done some years ago to determine what the most important factors were in positive outcomes in counseling. They discovered the most important factors were, in order: the motivation of the client, the relationship with the therapist, and then the type of therapy that was used. Hopefully this has been helpful when you are in need of a counselor.

NAVIGATING
LIFE
When and How to Involve a Professional

Book 1
In this book, you will discover what therapy is and how it helps heal anxiety, depression, PTSD, abuse and other mental, emotional problems. You will learn the difference between psychiatrists, psychologists and counselors and how medication works for mental health treatment. When you understand how counseling is done you will be more comfortable using the included suggestions for finding a counselor.

Book 2
In this book, you will learn about adoption, ADHD, autism, developmental delays in children and how to identify them, special needs, respite care and how to find special medical providers and primary care doctors. You will understand how to help your child using IEPs and 504 Accommodations and where to turn for support.

Book 3
In this book, you will learn about understanding personalities, fears, what to do prior to marriage, how to keep marriage working, the damage divorce causes, costs of going to counseling, why people don't go to counseling, what happens if they go or don't go, what marriage counseling is like, getting help in domestic abuse and the basics of parenting.

About the Author

With a degree in Psychology and Master's of Social Work, Craig has been practicing for 40 years in psychotherapy, marriage and family counseling. He has treated patients with varying mental/emotional disorders, including victims of sexual abuse. He was a foster parent for children with special needs and assisted parents who have children with special needs. He has worked with domestic and international adoptions for his entire career. He is the father of 7 children and 12 grandchildren. He loves being with his family and once this book is finished, he can't wait to get to the golf course.